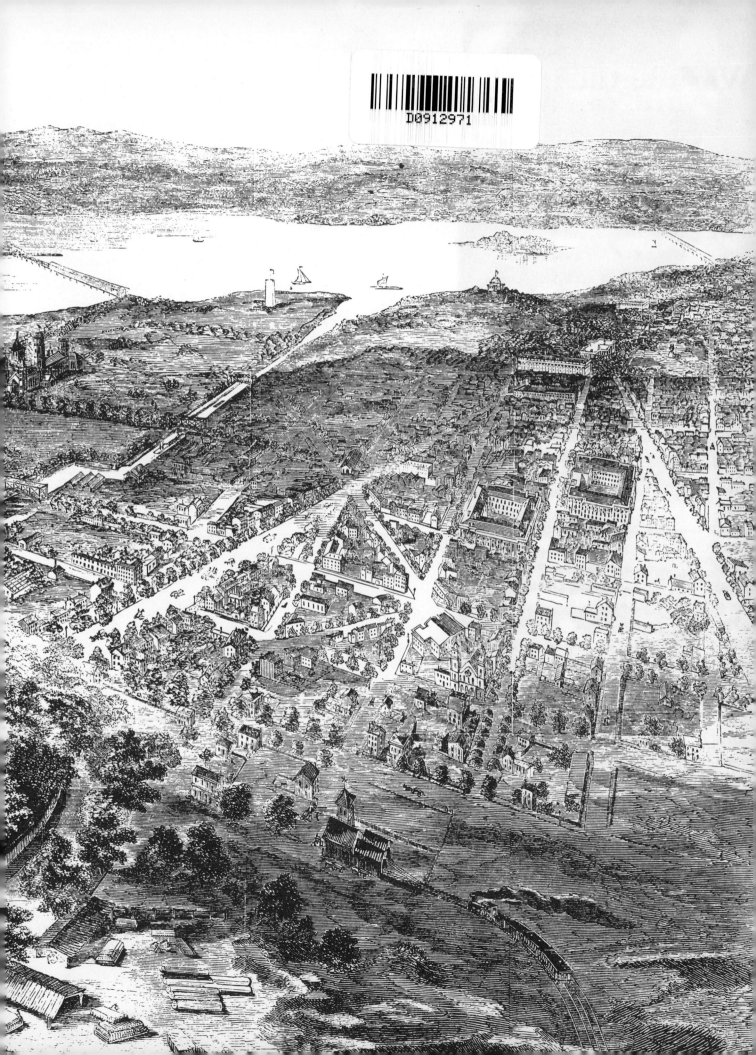

Washington D.C.

---❖---

THE STORY OF OUR NATION'S CAPITAL

Here, in words and pictures, is a lively record of our nation's capital, beginning in 1791 with an unpromising stretch of farmland. The United States was young and poor; but George Washington, Thomas Jefferson, and Pierre L'Enfant planned a magnificent capital for a great nation. This book shows what has happened to their great dream.

Here are the stirring and unusual events of Washington's history.

Here are intriguing facts about the village that grew to be the leading capital of the Western world.

And here, too, are the colorful men and women—scoundrels as well as heroes—who have made Washington what it is today.

Balloon view of Washington, D.C., from Harper's Weekly *July 27, 1861. (An interior view of the Capitol's roofless rotunda appears on page 53.)*

illustrated with photographs and maps

RANDOM HOUSE · NEW YORK

Washington D.C.

THE STORY OF OUR NATION'S CAPITAL

by Howard K. Smith

For helpful suggestions about the text and illustrations for this book, grateful acknowledgment is made to Josephine Cobb, Specialist in Iconography, National Archives, and Curator of the Columbia Historical Society; and to Milton Kaplan, Curator of Historical Prints, Library of Congress.

A passage is quoted from *Reveille in Washington* by Margaret Leech by permission of Harper & Row, Publishers, Incorporated. A passage is quoted and paraphrased from Robert Jungk's *Brighter Than a Thousand Suns* by permission of Harcourt, Brace & World, Inc.

PICTURE CREDITS: Arnold Studio, 12, 37; The Bettmann Archive, Inc., 49 (bot.), 64 (top), 88; Columbia Historical Society, 74; Culver Pictures, Inc., 59 (top), 60, 72; Diamond Art Studio, 182–183; Philip Gendreau, viii; The Granger Collection, 47, 50, 55 (bot.), 59 (bot.), 65 (bot. right), 66, 83, 87; Harris & Ewing, 114 (right), 116, 122, 126; Erich Hartmann, Magnum Photos, 67; Fritz Henle, Photo Researchers, vi; Historical Pictures Service, Chicago, 27, 29 (top), 45, 53, 57 (bot.), 70, 85 (bot.), 86 (top), 90, 94 (top), 96, 97, 99, 101, 107, 117 (bot.), 125; Henry E. Huntington Library and Art Gallery, San Marino, Calif., 46; Gordon Johnson, ii–iii, 35 (right), 41, 113, 137 (right); Keystone Press Agency, 91 (top), 118; Nina Leen, *Life* Magazine © Time, Inc., 6, 7; Library of Congress, endpapers, 4, 9, 13, 21, 31 (bot.), 32, 36, 39, 42, 55 (top), 57 (top), 63, 64 (bot.), 65 (top), 65 (bot. left and middle), 73, 77, 79, 92, 132; Litton Industries, Aero Service Division, 130; Maryland Historical Society, 26, 28; Metropolitan Museum of Art, gift of William H. Huntington, 1883, 25; National Archives, 2, 15, 40, 49 (top), 62, 69, 71, 89, 106; New York Public Library, 30, 31 (top), 38, 44, 61, 75; Robert Perron, 185; Theodore Roosevelt Association, 78; Abbie Rowe, National Park Service, 149; Sy Seidman, 19, 22, 23, 100, 117 (top); Robert Emmett Smallman, v, 35 (left), 81, 82 (top), 98, 112, 113, 170, 181, 187; Smithsonian Institution, 20 (bot.), 29 (bot.), 34, 43, 54, 68, 76, 82 (bot.), 91 (bot.), 95, 127, 159, 165; Michael D. Sullivan, Photo Researchers, i, 147; Underwood & Underwood, 105; United Press International Photo, 85 (top), 86 (bot.), 102, 103, 109, 119, 129, 135, 140, 144, 148, 156, 164, 173, 174; U.S. Army, 36; U.S. Coast and Geodetic Survey, 10–11; Valentine Museum, Cook Collection, 56; White House Collection, 20; Wide World Photos, 94 (bot.), 115, 120, 137 (left), 142, 143, 146, 150, 154, 161, 163, 167, 168, 171, 172, 175, 177, 179, 193; drawings by Gluyas Williams, copr. © 1942, *The New Yorker Magazine, Inc.*, 114 (right), 133.

COVER: *Declan Hawn, Black Star.*

TO MRS. LYNDON B. JOHNSON

CONTENTS

1 The Story of Peter Child   3

2 Flowers in the Desert   19

3 A Contemptible Hamlet   33

4 The Citadel: 1860-1865   46

5 Wall Street's Potomac Branch   68

6 The First World Crisis   80

7 Years of Blindness   92

8 That Man in the White House   108

9 The Arsenal of Democracy   124

10 A City on a Lonely Summit   141

11 Washington in Our Time   160

INDEX   188

Washington D.C.

THE STORY OF
OUR NATION'S CAPITAL

*A modern medallion
honoring Pierre L'Enfant.
(No authentic portrait
survives from his own day.)*

CHAPTER ONE
THE STORY OF PETER CHILD

THE SETTING

For a century and a third, March was the great month of the city of Washington. Until the time of Franklin D. Roosevelt, when the occasion was changed to January, March was the month in which Presidents were inaugurated and new beginnings were made.

But the first great thing that happened to the city in March was its birth. What was to become Washington was then a large tract of rolling Maryland countryside, locked in a notch created by the Potomac River and its tributary, the Anacostia (then called the Eastern Branch). It was very thinly dotted with a few wooden farmhouses.

South of what was to become Washington, and on the Virginia side of the Potomac, was the handsome little tobacco-shipping port of Alexandria. Its pattern of streets had been laid out in 1749 by the 17-year-old brother of a prominent planter, Lawrence Washington. The brother's name was George.

And west of what was to be Washington, and on the Maryland side of the river, was the pretty little tobacco port of George, laid out in 1751 and named after King George II of England. Shortly it would be called George Town, and then Georgetown.

Both little towns are still there and look remarkably similar to the way they looked then. But the sparsely peopled rolling hills in between were destined to change beyond all recognition.

THE VISITOR

Early in March, 1791, George Town took note of an impressive visitor. Those who saw him described him as being tall and having an erect military bearing. He was a Frenchman who had adopted

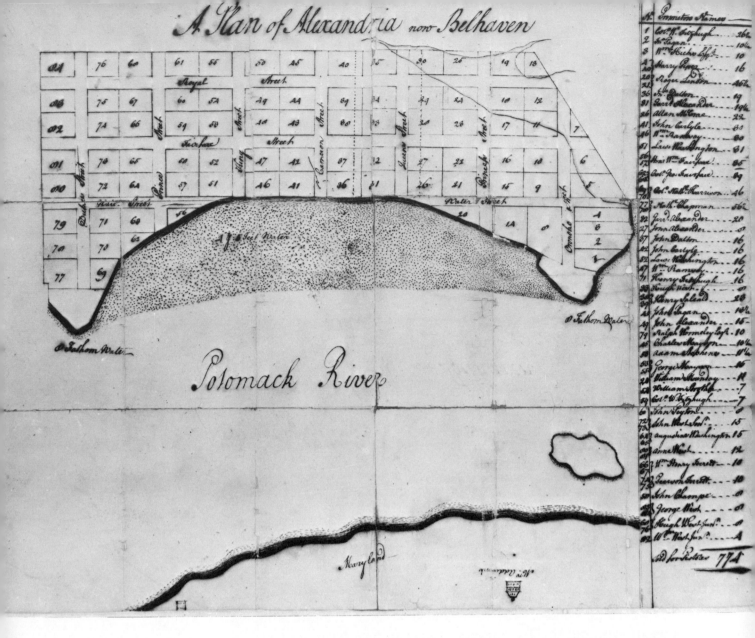

A Plan of Alexandria now Belhaven

Plan of Alexandria, drawn by a 17-year-old surveyor, George Washington. Many years later, for the city named in his honor, he would choose a site across the Potomac—only a few miles from his own beloved Mount Vernon.

the new nation in America as his country. In one respect he resembled two other famous Frenchmen—Cyrano de Bergerac a century before him, and Charles de Gaulle two centuries later: He had a large and impressive nose. Also like those two Frenchmen he was proud, cultivated, and self-assured.

His name was Pierre Charles L'Enfant. It is an awkward name for Americans to pronounce. President Washington, whose orders the visitor carried, spelled and pronounced it Lanfang. Newspapers spelled it Longfont. It is a pity that they could not simply translate it into English and call him Peter Child. But L'Enfant was his name. He liked it; he was about to cover it with enduring fame; so L'Enfant it had to be.

L'Enfant was one of those rare personalities who upon entering a room command attention by sheer presence. On this occasion, the impression he made must have been stronger than usual. The weather was bad, so he would have been wearing the long great-coat favored by officers in the Revolutionary War. And as his coach from New York had broken down and he had proceeded on foot and on horseback, he was undoubtedly spattered with red clay mud.

He was an ardent and impatient man, so we may guess that he was vexed—not so much by the journey behind him as by the prospect ahead: The wooded hills south of George Town were blanked out by dense fog. Fog alternated with driving rain. When rain and fog relented later, there came an unseasonal snowfall, and the swollen Potomac flooded the region. L'Enfant's problem was that President Washington was soon to drive down from Philadelphia. Before going on to his plantation at Mount Vernon, the President would stop in George Town to review L'Enfant's progress. The Frenchman had about three weeks to design a city to cover an area he could not see because of bad weather.

He wrote to the Secretary of State, Thomas Jefferson, that "if by Monday next the weather does not change," he would inspect the terrain "by riding over it on horseback as I have already done yesterday through the rain." The weather changed only for the worse. So he made not one but many wet rides back and forth over the hills. One night when his spirit was as warm as his clothes were wet, he wrote to the Secretary of the Treasury, Alexander Hamilton, "As there is no doubt I must feel highly interested in the success of the undertaking, I become apprehensive of being charged with partiality when I assure you that no position in America can be more susceptible of grand improvement than that between the Eastern Branch of the Potomac and Georgetown."

That was the nicest thing to be said about the area for nearly a hundred years. But L'Enfant possessed a special gift of imagination that could penetrate the future.

WHY THE POTOMAC

Why was a city planned at this unlikely spot? Three men were chiefly responsible—President Washington, Secretary of State Jefferson, and L'Enfant.

When George Washington was a young surveyor, he often rode the low hills of the region and had come to love it. As a colonial officer in the British Army, he was assigned to ride to Fort Duquesne (now Pittsburgh). It occurred to him that a city on the Potomac would be nearer to Fort Duquesne and better able

6

George Washington

to tap the riches of the Old West in Ohio than any existing Eastern seaport.

When George Washington became President in 1789 and more than a dozen existing cities asked to become the capital city, he was troubled by their jealousies. At one time, when the capital was located in Philadelphia, some unpaid war veterans threatened the Congress. The local authorities, devoted entirely to local concerns, refused protection. So it was decided that the federal government should have its very own capital in a city it would create. George Washington immediately thought of the banks of the Potomac. But even then the nation was spiritually divided between North and South. The Potomac was in the South, so Northern members of Congress resisted the choice. A little shrewd politics had to be applied by the second of the three men who made Washington the capital.

HOW THE POTOMAC

Secretary of State Jefferson—lean, red-haired, ever questioning— was widely deemed to be a radical. But he had an extremely aristocratic taste in foods and wines, as in houses. One day when the new Union of States seemed about to break apart in anger, he invited his chief political rival, Secretary of the Treasury Hamilton, to dine with him in his home in New York, then the temporary capital. He also invited two fellow Virginia politicians. The dinner consisted of "savoury viands" and several kinds of wine. It took place in May of 1790, nearly a year before L'Enfant's trip to the Potomac. It was one of the most successful dinners ever held. When the four men rose from the table, the argument was settled. The capital of the new nation would be on the Potomac.

Briefly, the threat to unity was this: During the Revolutionary

Thomas Jefferson.
A great French sculptor,
Jean Houdon, made this bust
when Jefferson was in
France in 1789. Five years
earlier on a visit to the
United States, Houdon
made the bust of George
Washington shown on
the facing page.

War the individual states had raised their own funds and incurred their separate debts. Now Hamilton wanted the central government to take over all the debts. He favored a strong federal government and felt that this would give it special authority. The Southern states refused. They had few debts; the Northern states had many. So the North would gain from Hamilton's plan.

At the famous dinner, Jefferson suggested that the South would agree to Hamilton's financial plan—if the Northerners would accept the Potomac location for the new capital. Hamilton agreed to muster Northern votes for that purpose. So the two Southern delegates agreed to Hamilton's financial plan. But, said Jefferson, one of his fellow Virginians agreed only "with a revulsion of stomach almost convulsive."

In July, 1790, Congress voted to ask the President to designate the exact location he preferred on the Potomac.

So Washington and Jefferson launched the idea. But the main credit belongs to L'Enfant. Without his triumphant design the many shocks the young Republic was to suffer would have jarred the capital loose and into some other location.

RIPENING GENIUS

Who was Pierre L'Enfant? He was a creature of his times. In the late 1700s there was a special hunger among well-educated young Europeans to trust in reason. They thought governments should be chosen by free judgment rather than imposed from above. When the American colonies rose up against arbitrary government, ardent spirits were set afire all over Europe. In France, in Prussia, in Poland, young men sought passage to America to volunteer in the Revolutionary armies. Most volunteers came from France, and one of the very first—well before his more famous compatriot, the Marquis de Lafayette—was Pierre L'Enfant.

He fought well, was severely wounded, was taken prisoner, and then returned to the American side in a prisoner exchange. He rose from lieutenant to major.

L'Enfant was a gifted artist. He had been taught by his father, a painter of battle scenes and landscapes for the King of France. In the famous bitter winter at Valley Forge, L'Enfant busied himself sketching soldiers. The sketches impressed General Washington, who kept L'Enfant in mind after that.

After victory and a brief visit back to France, L'Enfant settled in the prosperous city of New York. He designed the Federal Hall, where our wandering government stayed awhile. It was generally thought the finest building in young America. He also designed medals, including the Order of the Purple Heart, which today is awarded to American soldiers wounded in combat. He even planned a pageant to persuade the citizens of New York to ratify the newly drafted Constitution of the United States.

For the first capital of the United States, New York City, Pierre L'Enfant designed Federal Hall. On the balcony, in 1789, George Washington was inaugurated as first President of the new nation.

Contracts became more numerous, and the Major could look forward to a prosperous life in a sophisticated community. But then came an announcement that completely unsettled him. He abandoned New York and riches. He even rejected a commission by Alexander Hamilton to design the new nation's first coins. The announcement was that the new nation had agreed on the unique idea of creating a city of its own. L'Enfant sat down and wrote to President Washington:

"Sir, the late determination of Congress to lay the foundation of a city which is to become the capital of this vast empire offers so great an occasion of acquiring reputation to whoever may be appointed to conduct the execution of the business that your Excellency will not be surprised that my ambition and the desire I have of being a useful citizen should lead me to wish a share in the undertaking.

"Although the means now within the power of the country are not such as to pursue the design to any great extent, it will be obvious that the plan should be drawn on such a scale as to leave room for the aggrandizement and embellishment which the increase of the wealth of the nation will permit it to pursue at any period however remote."

On the next two pages: L'Enfant's plan for Washington, D.C. The President's House and the Capitol (which he called "Congress House") were built in the next few years on the sites planned by L'Enfant. But the Washington Monument (A), built much later, had to be placed off center on firmer ground. To see how L'Enfant's plan has been carried out, turn to the map on pages 182–183.

GEORGE TOWN.

N° 15.

N° 2.

E.   E.

President's house.

E.

D.

S 4

L

A

Canal   through Tiber Creek

H   H

N° 3.

C

POTOWMAC RIVER.

Road to Alexandria.

OF VIRGINIA. WITHIN THE FEDER

principal,
long Avenues

Squares &c.
on the
enues

... ies in the
... the improv

... different States may
... were conspicuous in
... general imitation: to
... thought proper & celebrate
... m each other, and as equally
... ments, and as contiguous to
... ments' round those Squares must

... grand idea of   patriotic interest

we tering th it part of the City, its overplus
will fall, from under the base of that
Edifice, and in a Casca de of 20 feet in
height, and 50 in breadth into the
reservoir below; thence to run
in three falls through the
Garden into the
ground Canal.

The perpendicular height
of the Ground where the Congress
house stands, is above the tide of
Tiber Creek, 78 feet.

Perpendicular height of the West branch
above the tide in Tiber Creek?

F. I. P.ts
115. 7. 2/8

New Road to Bladensburg.

Lat. Congr
Long.

Bridge.

Congress
house.

E.

Draw Bridge.

Canal

Canal to the man's.

Canal to the Market.

EASTERN BRANCH.

RYLAND, WITHIN THE FE

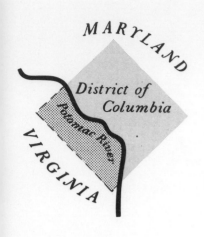

Ellicott and Banneker laid out an area of 100 square miles for the District of Columbia. Since 1846, when the darker area was returned to Virginia, the District has contained 69 square miles.

L'Enfant's enthusiasm and his grasp of the idea appealed to the President. When Jefferson had worked his political magic and all was agreed, L'Enfant was sent splashing through rain and mud to the Potomac.

THE PLAN

One month after L'Enfant arrived in George Town, a surveyor from Philadelphia named Andrew Ellicott laid the boundary stones of the district to be called Columbia. He imbedded the first stone in the Virginia bank of the Potomac at a place called Jones Point, south of Alexandria. The original stone is still there, half buried in Potomac mud at high tide. So are several of the other stones that mark the ten-mile-square Federal District. Ellicott was aided by a brilliant Negro named Benjamin Banneker, described in a newspaper of the time as "an Ethiopian" with great "abilities as surveyor and astronomer." Today there exists in the city a school named after Banneker.

The District of Columbia is now humid and hot in the summer. Visitors have often wondered why George Washington chose so uncomfortable a location. The answer is that in those days it was a pleasant place all year round, as it is now three seasons of the year. Then the Potomac was clear, and its banks and hills thickly patched with trees. When builders later removed the trees and bushes, and rain began washing the red soil down into the river, and human beings began pouring pollution into it—only then did the river become dirty and the city grow humid and uncomfortable.

At that time a creek cut through the area. At first it was known as Goose Creek. But a farmer named Pope came to own most of its length. He could not resist calling his farm Rome and rechristening the creek the Tiber. In those days the Tiber was a clear creek. But as the population grew it was used as a kind of open sewer. In our time it has been covered over, and Constitution Avenue now marks much of its course. From the soil washed down into it and the Potomac, dry land has been created, and the Lincoln and Jefferson memorials are now located on that artificially created land.

L'Enfant drew a grid of city blocks over the area. In addition to streets on a square block pattern, he cut diagonal avenues to link the main hills. The east-west streets were given alphabetical names—C Street, D Street, and so on. The north-south streets were given numbered names—14th Street, 15th Street, and so on.

And the diagonal avenues were named after states. L'Enfant insisted that the streets be very broad. A broad street in most cities at that time would have been no more than 50 feet across. But he wanted 90 and 130 feet for the width of ordinary streets, and from 180 to 400 feet for very broad ones.

This web of cross and diagonal ways was draped mainly over two hills. One was called Jenkins Hill, then densely covered with woods. In a letter to Jefferson, L'Enfant called this rise "a pedestal waiting for a monument." On it the Congress House, or Capitol, was to be constructed. The second hill was a mile and a half away. A fruit orchard covered it. There L'Enfant wanted to build the President's Palace, later to be called the White House.

The two hills were linked with a broad street, called Pennsylvania Avenue to placate the state which had clamored to be the center of government. It is the ceremonial street along which inaugural processions pass. The two elevations were to be linked also by two huge parks. One would stretch south from the President's Palace, and from the Congress House westward would be another, to be called the Mall. Where they crossed L'Enfant planned to have a statue of President Washington on horseback. The statue was never erected. Instead, several decades later, the tall Washington Monument was put there—or near there, for the soil was so soft at the real crossing-point that the stone monument had to be placed somewhat off center on firmer ground.

The L'Enfant plan had many other interesting features—for example, a waterfall from Capitol Hill down the Mall, made by piping together the hill's many gushing springs.

The Old Stone House

This was the plan which the Frenchman laid before Washington when the President stopped in George Town. They are said to have gone over the rough sketch in what is called the Old Stone House, which may still be seen on M Street. Washington later said the plan aroused "universal applause." And Jefferson sent copies to all foreign capitals for proud display.

THE SPIRIT

The greatest enemy of L'Enfant's plan was Doubt. It took a very imaginative eye to look upon hills and fields and pigsties and imagine a spacious, beautiful city like Paris or St. Petersburg. The average American planter or merchant was apt to think the idea grandiose and impossible to carry out. So L'Enfant wanted to provide quick and convincing evidence that the city would be completed. Here are some of his proposals:

Give each of the states a city block to itself on condition it build handsomely and promptly. Give a square to each foreign embassy on the same condition. Pride would cause each to vie with the others, and a score of handsome buildings would rapidly go up. Once many grand buildings were there, the breadth of the streets would be respected. But if structures did not go up quickly, farmers would complain that too much land was taken up by broad streets, and they would encroach on them and narrow them down. L'Enfant also proposed that the government not sell lots in the city immediately. Instead, it should borrow money and wait until many buildings were up and the value of the lots had multiplied. He feared that early sales would allow speculators to buy the land cheaply and hold it for high profits later.

This approach took a certain boldness. At that time in the wilderness on the Potomac almost the only boldness was in L'Enfant's own bosom. So most of his proposals were disregarded.

GETTING THE LAND

The area included in the Major's design was at that time owned by nineteen farmers. The plan for obtaining land from them was ingenious. It was pointed out to them that their land would multiply in value as the city grew. The federal government therefore asked the owners to cede half their holdings to the government at a price of 25 Maryland pounds (about $66) an acre. In addition, all areas L'Enfant marked off as streets or parks would be given to the government free of charge. The rise in value of what remained would more than repay the farmers for what they gave up.

There was much bargaining. Once George Washington himself had to negotiate. One farmer was especially difficult—Davey Burnes, a Scotsman who owned a farm covering the land between what is now Constitution Avenue and the White House. It is said that the President approached the farmer and argued that, but for the federal city rising there, his farm would be worthless. To which Burnes replied that, but for Washington having married the rich widow Custis, he too would not be worth much. But the prospect of riches prevailed with Burnes, and Washington was able to tell his cabinet that all had come round—"even the obdurate Mr. Burnes."

Many landowners lost money by the arrangement, for the city grew in some directions and failed to grow in others. But Burnes was one of those who became very rich. His daughter Marcia married General Van Ness of New York, and much later they built the finest private house in the city, on the site where the Pan American Union stands today.

TROUBLE

George Washington was busy in Philadelphia running a nation. To manage the business of raising a capital city on the Potomac, he had appointed three commissioners in January, 1791. They were L'Enfant's bosses on the scene, and an unpromising lot they were.

One commissioner was Daniel Carroll of Carrollton. He was the uncle of the biggest local landowner, Daniel Carroll of Duddington, who owned the land around Capitol Hill. He openly said that he would side with his nephew in any conflicts, no matter what the rights and wrongs! Another commissioner was a planter accused by his fellows of "derangement of mind" because of his difficulty in getting along with people. And the third was George Washington's doctor, whose attitude is typified by his opposition to the plans for a large park around the White House: He said it would lead to despotism.

Daniel Carroll and the other two commissioners signed the bill of sale for L'Enfant's own lot in the new city.

AT a public Sale of Lots in the City of WASHINGTON, *Peter Charles L'Enfant of George Town Maryland* became purchaser of Lot number *thirty* in square number *one hundred twenty seven* for the confideration of *ninety nine pounds twelve money of Maryland* on the terms and conditions publifhed at the fame fale: And he hath accordingly paid one-fourth part of the faid confideration money, and given Bond, with fecurity, for the payment of the refidue; on the payment whereof, with intereft, according to the faid Bond the faid *Peter Charles L'Enfant* or his affigns will be entitled to a conveyance in fee.

18th October 1791

Square No 127. Lot No 30

Th John Jed

D. Stuart Commrs.

Danl Carroll

199

Friction began at once. The first trouble was over the breadth of the streets and the number of public parks. The commissioners asked L'Enfant to reduce both. He refused. Next, the commissioners ordered an early sale of lots to the public. L'Enfant resisted, saying the lots were worth little now and should be held until they were worth much more. He also withheld his design for the city; he wanted to prevent speculators from buying the best future sites to hold for high profits later. The commissioners protested to President Washington, who supported them.

Next came a more dramatic conflict. Carroll of Duddington persisted in building himself a farmhouse on a location agreed by deed to become what is today Garfield Park near the Capitol. L'Enfant wrote the landowner two letters advising him of his violation but got an answer to neither. So the Major sent workmen, carefully dismantled the structure, and moved the materials off the plot in question. The commissioners were furious. It was insufferable to have a fastidious foreigner act so forcibly against a fellow planter. But L'Enfant prevailed.

The next great conflict was crucial. His plan now complete, the Major planned to go to the temporary capital in Philadelphia and present all details to the President. He left his chief assistant in charge, telling him to hire workmen, bring in building stone, and proceed without delay to clear streets of trees and lay foundations for buildings. When L'Enfant had departed, the commissioners ordered the assistant to dismiss the workers and stop work. They argued that it would be too costly to dig in the winter earth. The assistant, puzzled about whom to obey but infected with L'Enfant's wish to move quickly, disregarded the commissioners and went on working. The commissioners were furious again. They had him arrested and jailed for "trespassing."

When the Major heard of this in Philadelphia, he insisted that he be granted authority to direct the work. Washington and Jefferson, plagued with other worries, sided with their fellow planters. L'Enfant was dismissed less than a year after he had begun his work.

A JUDGMENT

The creator of Washington has been criticized for being grandiose in his designs, for being uncompromising about them, and for having a difficult temperament. In fact, all three qualities were required to fulfill his assignment. The plan had to be done on a grand scale or not at all. Any compromise at the start would have led to an erosion of the plan. There is no evidence that L'Enfant was more temperamental and insistent than any good architect would be today.

Charles Moore, who a century later became the city's chief planner, expressed the opinion that if George Washington had been present himself in the beginning city, he would have supported L'Enfant. One of Washington's last wishes was: Don't change the plan.

One author who has written on the subject suggests that the proper attitude for the President would have been that adopted a century later by Theodore Roosevelt during the building of the Panama Canal. When the canal commissioners proved too plodding, the chief engineer complained to President Roosevelt. The President answered, "I sent you down to build a canal. I want it built. Do what you consider necessary to this end and report afterwards to the commissioners."

Andrew Ellicott was appointed by the commissioners to replace L'Enfant, but he found them impossible to serve and quit within a year. It is also noteworthy that those most intimately concerned —the Washington landowners—wrote President Washington and begged him to reinstate L'Enfant, for only in him did they have trust.

Meanwhile, L'Enfant's fears turned out to be justified. The sale of lots was a failure, for the plots had as yet little worth. Speculators did buy up most of the city; then they went bankrupt and gave the city a bad name as an investment. And the city failed for a long time to attract inhabitants and to prosper.

A HERO AND A GENTLEMAN

Republics are often ungrateful to their servants. When the break with L'Enfant came, President Washington expressed fear that L'Enfant would open a public attack on the city and damage it. The President also ordered guards posted lest the Major pull out the stakes marking future streets in the wilderness. The father of our country must have felt a little ashamed when the Frenchman not only took no destructive action, but sealed his lips for seven years lest he tarnish the President's good name.

At no time, before or during the work, did L'Enfant set a price for his services or show any interest in monetary return. He must have been deeply offended when the first engraved map of his city was published bearing the name of Andrew Ellicott, without even a mention of its real creator. Congress voted L'Enfant a small compensation. He rejected it. Late in life he was impoverished and applied for compensation a good deal higher than that offered by Congress, but by any assessment lower than he deserved. Congress did not act on it.

L'Enfant undertook many private contracts, the last one, oddly, with the son-in-law of his old enemy, Daniel Carroll of Duddington—William D. Digges, owner of Green Hill just outside the District. Those who saw him at the time describe Pierre L'Enfant as tall and thin, with his hair pomaded down close to his head. He always carried a hickory cane with a silver head, and his gracious manners persisted. He died at the age of seventy-one on June 14, 1825. His total possessions added up to $45 in worth. He was buried at the foot of a tree at Digges' mansion, where his body lay for three-quarters of a century.

Then Americans began to understand his achievement and its value to the nation. In 1902 a Senate committee reported that "the original plan of the city of Washington, having stood the test of a century, has met universal approval. The departures from that plan are to be regretted, and wherever possible remedied."

L'Enfant's remains were removed from their obscure resting place to Arlington hill overlooking his city, with first a pause in the rotunda of the Capitol, where citizens might pass and honor him as they have honored dead Presidents like Lincoln and Kennedy. When his body was put in its final resting place, Secretary of State Elihu Root said, "It is not a change in L'Enfant that brings us here. It is we who have changed, who have just become able to appreciate his work. And our tribute should be to continue his work."

The Republic has produced a number of heroes, a number of gentlemen, and a few geniuses. L'Enfant had to wait a century, but at last he was recognized as being all three.

CHAPTER TWO
FLOWERS IN THE DESERT

NOWHERE-UPON-POTOMAC

A law passed by Congress required that the government cease its wanderings and settle in Washington—ready or not—in the year 1800.

In June of that year, sloops carrying records and furnishings from Philadelphia sailed up the Potomac. They passed Mount Vernon, always stately on its high hill but now also sad, for the first President had died there six months earlier.

They passed the bustling town of Alexandria on the west bank. And then they passed the federal "city" on the east bank. Washington had a scattered population of around 3,000 in contrast to Alexandria's compact community of 5,000. Nine years after L'Enfant designed his bold plan, the capital city had 372 houses, most of them wooden. Of all these houses, only the White House and part of the Capitol building and a handsome private residence near the White House—later known as the Octagon House—are still there.

George Washington's coffin at Mount Vernon.

From shipboard the area appeared wooded and pleasantly rural. But when the ships were unloaded at Lear's Wharf (near the site of the John F. Kennedy cultural center today), and overseers drove the carts out Pennsylvania Avenue to the White House and then to the Capitol, the view was desolate indeed. The avenue was imaginary. Forests and stumps and Davey Burnes' corn crops filled most of it up to the White House. From there to Capitol Hill most of it belonged to the marshy bank of Tiber Creek, and the carts had to make a long detour. Wherever building had taken place there were big ugly patches of litter and muddy holes.

Near the White House were boardinghouses for the total of

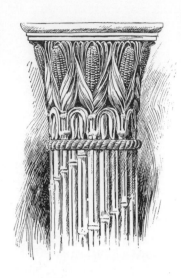

American capitals for Greek columns: corn (above) and tobacco (below).

seemed a mere wart on so vast a structure, so the present high dome, made of cast iron sections, was built. Changes would continue right into our own day.

Each rebuilding or addition has been done in richer materials, measuring the rising wealth of the nation. First the foundation, buried deep in the earth, was made of chunks of granite blasted from what was then called Braddock's Rock, in the Potomac off George Town. The rock has long since been blasted out of existence, but fragments of it may still be found littering the Potomac shore. Its relatives are the Three Sisters rocks that jut out of the middle of the river there today.

The Capitol building itself was constructed of sandstone quarried in Acquia Creek, downstream in Virginia. The soft, crumbly stone had to be given many coats of paint (grey on the Capitol, white on the White House) to protect it from the weather. Inside the Capitol, the walls and decorative columns were first made of plaster and wood. When they were rebuilt later, they were made of sandstone. When they were rebuilt again, they were made of marble.

In the sandstone stage a designer, Benjamin Latrobe, created capitals for the internal columns resembling those of ancient Greece, but Americanized with corn tassels or tobacco leaves in place of acanthus leaves. These column tops, Latrobe said, "obtained me more applause from members of Congress than all the works of magnitude and difficulty that surrounded them." They are still there and still admired.

When Congress arrived in 1800, only the square Senate wing was finished. The central portion with its dome did not yet exist. The House side was just beginning to rise from its foundations. On the walls of the lone finished section were hung two portraits, one of Louis XVI of France, and one of his wife, Marie Antoinette. Both had been beheaded seven years earlier, but these Royalist gifts were all the young Republic had to display.

Into this lone wing were packed the Senate, the House, the Library of Congress, and later the Supreme Court. The wing was also used as a church on Sundays. Probably we have received more value from this structure, which cost only forty-two cents a cubic foot to build, than from any other ever erected in the United States.

Almost immediately the Capitol became what it has been ever since—a theater for dramatic decisions. The month President Adams moved to Washington a Presidential election was held.

Adams, the Federalist (Conservative), was defeated. In electoral votes, two Republicans (now called Democrats) tied: Jefferson and Aaron Burr. In accordance with the Constitution, the election was given to the House of Representatives to decide.

On February 11, 1801, while snow swirled outside, the House began voting. In six days it voted thirty-five times without giving either man a clear majority. The members, who had been miserable in their crowded and uncomfortable surroundings, forgot their discomfort in the general excitement. Amid the voting Adams, who could throw Federalist votes either way, said to Jefferson, whom he hated:

"Sir, the event of the election is within your own power. You have only to say you will do justice to the public creditors, maintain the navy, and not disturb those holding office, and the government will instantly be put in your hands."

Jefferson answered, "I will not come into the government by capitulation."

"Then," said Adams, "things must take their course."

Things did, and on the thirty-sixth ballot Jefferson was elected third President of the United States.

Being President-elect, Jefferson was allowed in his boarding-house not only a bedroom but a sitting room too. On March 4, accompanied by friends, he walked on a path of marble chips through the mud to the Capitol to be sworn in. Bitter John Adams took no part. He was leaving the White House and the city in his carriage when he heard cannon announcing the new President's term.

When Congress arrived in 1800, the Senate, the House, and the Library of Congress all had to crowd together in the Senate wing (at right). This picture, made a little later, shows the House wing almost completed.

After inauguration, Jefferson went to the White House and did not return to the Hill. He gave up the practice of going to Congress to read his messages. His excuse was the difficulty of traversing Pennsylvania Avenue, which was still a bog. His real reason for having others read his messages may have been that he, who did everything else well, did not read aloud well. He would not have been a good television debater. (The practice of the President's going in person to the Hill to read his message was not resumed until 1913, when Woodrow Wilson, a marvelous orator, went there. Since then all Presidents have followed Wilson's example.)

Shortly before Jefferson's inauguration, Jenkins Heights had been a wilderness impenetrable even to roaming cows and chickens. Now it was never again to know solitude. It became the crucible of strife and argument and maneuver and pressure from which the will of millions was distilled into legislative action. Mighty interests brought riches there to influence and even to corrupt. There honest men were to insist upon principle to the point of committing political suicide, and their stories were to be told by a youthful Senator in a book called *Profiles in Courage*. The great, unreckonable perils of man governing himself were to be risked there fully for the first time on earth. Repeatedly the question was to be asked, Can such a government survive? With faults and failures and some ignominies counted in, the net answer so far has been a glorious affirmative.

PALACE OF THE SACRIFICIAL OFFERING

In ancient times in Peru there was a civilization which at intervals selected its outstanding youth, clothed him in beautiful array, bathed him in scented oils, worshipped him—then hurled him down into a pit to die.

Though rather more logical reasons were cited for it, the new nation adopted a somewhat similar procedure. By a vast screening process it selected, and still selects, at intervals its prince among men, inaugurates him, installs him in a fine mansion surrounded by ceremony and power, celebrates him—and then gradually tears him to pieces.

It is a fact that in the large Georgian mansion set above Tiber Creek there has been a good deal more sorrow than joy. Normally, a President enters the White House enjoying a portion of love, for without it he could not have been elected. Normally, he uses up that good will as an investor would a bank account—to get some necessary things done. Normally, at the end of his term he has used it up, is no longer popular, is tired, beaten, and squeezed dry. Democracy is often a tragedy.

The house where this takes place was first called the President's Palace and later the Executive Mansion. It was not until the 1900s that a man who changed much else to suit the people also induced Congress to change the official name of the mansion to the popular one. Theodore Roosevelt made it legally the White House.

The first President to enter it did so in certain knowledge that his portion of love was already exhausted. Within weeks, John Adams was rejected at the polls. And his short stay in the White House was further ruined by the news of his son's death in New York, received the same day he lost the election.

Thomas Jefferson came in a lonely, widowed man. When he left, he was impoverished and had only the joy of release from years of unrelenting strife. There is something touching in the fact that the two bitter enemies, Jefferson and Adams, became regular correspondents and friends-by-mail when the bond of having both been used up in the White House had been created between them. On July 4, 1826, Jefferson died at Monticello in Virginia. A few hours later, on the same day, Adams died in Quincy, Massachusetts.

John Adams, first President to occupy the White House.

Poets have told better than historians the story of the sad giant who lived in the White House when war for the Union was killing more Americans than would be killed in both World Wars of our time together. Lincoln was often criticized for making jokes, and only in an unguarded moment did he break down and confess—if he did not laugh he would cry.

Until our own times, the story has generally been the same. Harry Truman called it "the big white jail on Pennsylvania Avenue." A cartoonist showed Eisenhower in his last year as a solitary prison inmate marking off the days on his wall. John Kennedy, the handsomest President, lay within its walls so mangled that his coffin could not be opened to a sorrowing public. The case of Theodore Roosevelt was unique. No one else ever left the house saying and meaning, "I enjoyed every moment!"

Work on the White House began in 1792. The design for the house had been chosen in a competition. One of the designs that failed was initialled "A.Z."—initials that disguised Thomas Jefferson, it was later learned. James Hoban, an Irishman then living in Charleston, South Carolina, won. His later ideas were not completely carried out, which may be fortunate, for he called for two wings to be added to the present structure. Three Presidents later

James Hoban's prizewinning design for the President's House. This is the north front, facing Lafayette Square. (President Andrew Jackson later added the North Portico, shown on page 88.)

Thomas Jefferson's unsuccessful design.

had plans drawn up for wings; all dropped the idea, for which posterity may be grateful. The addition or subtraction of anything would make the White House less dignified than it is.

It took a very long time to complete the house. For many years, the entrances were reached by temporary wooden steps and the roof leaked. Every President has wrought changes. Twice the White House entrails have been completely removed—once when the British burned it, and once when President Truman found it was about to collapse because so many beams and joists had been bored through for wires and pipes. But the walls have remained the same and have had the magical quality of generally making the men who live there greater than they were before.

Inhabitants of the White House have never been permitted to forget that it is the people's house, only on loan to the Presidents. From the beginning, the public has had a freedom of access such as is allowed in no royal or executive mansion anywhere else. At Thomas Jefferson's second inauguration, an English visitor said that "all who chose attended and even towards the close dirty boys who drank his wines and lolled upon his couches before us." That was probably an exaggeration.

The White House has been a home of sorrow. Yet no one with a serious chance of taking up the lease has ever turned it down. Jefferson called the job a "splendid misery," but the accent is on the adjective, not the noun.

And from the first moment people noticed something special about its occupant. The nation's government was meant to be a delicate balance of powers between three branches. But in fact, when they balanced, the government did not work well. When the Senate overbalanced, as after the Civil War, it worked badly. Only when the Presidency overbalanced the others—when leadership was clearly centered in the White House—only then was the nation well run.

THE THORNY THIRD BRANCH

Our Constitution created three branches of the federal government: the Executive (the President), the Legislative (Congress) and the Judicial branch (with the Supreme Court at the top). Although the Constitution meant them to be coequal in power, the third branch settled in third rank from the time of its creation in 1789. But in the year 1800, a remarkable American came to dominate the Supreme Court, and he elevated it to a place of great power.

When you visit the Capitol, make a point of going to the original Senate chamber. The Senate has long since moved to larger quarters, and the semicircular old room is now an occasional committee room. Around its walls you will see a series of marble busts. Follow them until you come to a face that looks like a weather map on an unusually turbulent day. That will be the face of John Marshall.

That was the face that Jefferson looked into, with a hatred that was mutual, when he was sworn in as President in 1801. Jefferson, born an aristocrat, was a radical democrat. Marshall, born poor in a log cabin, was a conservative aristocrat. They were relatives, which did not help. They were both uncommonly great men, which did not help either.

John Marshall had been Secretary of State under John Adams. When Adams and his party were overwhelmingly defeated in the election of 1800, Adams appointed Marshall Chief Justice of the United States. He hastily made many other judicial appointments —"midnight judges" they were called, because he signed their commissions just before midnight when he had to give up the Presidency to Thomas Jefferson.

Jefferson was furious. This was a defiance of the people's will. The judges, all of a rejected party, were there for life, a permanent brake on the will of the people. Jefferson even persuaded the House of Representatives to impeach one of the Supreme Court Justices. If the Senate had convicted the Justice of wrongdoing, there is no doubt that Jefferson would then have tried to eliminate Marshall and his other judicial opponents. But the impeached Justice was acquitted, so Jefferson gave up. It is good that he failed. For Marshall proceeded to make the Court a tool for tightening the union of

The great Chief Justice, John Marshall. By strengthening the Supreme Court, he also strengthened the young federal government.

states, and from that process Jefferson benefited greatly.

Before Marshall the third branch of the government had little prestige. One Chief Justice spent much of his term in Paris and another lived in London, suggesting that the post was a job without serious duties. When the Court moved to Washington in 1801—the last federal institution to move—no one had prepared a building for it on the site L'Enfant had set aside. The Senate offered it the small office of the clerk of the Senate, and there the Supreme Court went into session. It did not have a building of its own until 1935.

During those early years in Washington, the chief event that shaped the nation's great destiny was the purchase of Louisiana from the French. But almost equally important was the series of rulings handed down by John Marshall's Supreme Court. In one ruling, Marshall established the power of the Supreme Court to declare whether an action or piece of legislation was constitutional or not. This was in the famous case of *Marbury versus Madison*. Shrewdly, Marshall stated this power of the Court in a case in which he gave Jefferson the victory.

Having thus greatly enlarged the power of the Court, Marshall used it in every case to strengthen the federal government against state governments, and to strengthen the executive power within the government. At a time when unity was weak and the states ready to break away at any moment, he worked to bind the new nation together.

Benjamin Latrobe's design for chairs for the Madisons. The chairs were destroyed in the White House fire of 1814.

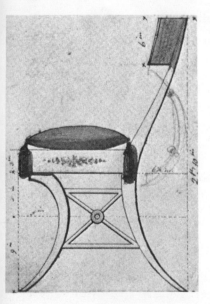

The great Louisiana Purchase itself was legalized by a Marshall ruling. Jefferson had sent envoys to Paris to try to buy the port of New Orleans from Napoleon. His envoys, to their surprise, were offered instead the whole Louisiana territory, a quarter of what would be the continental United States. The price was fifteen million dollars, working out at three cents an acre, the best real estate deal in history. Jefferson did not believe the Constitution allowed a President the power to make this deal. But he could not resist it. He was, a writer said, "by turns pleased, shaken, shocked, amazed and perturbed" at the presumed illegality of the move he was drawn into. It took the brilliant Marshall to hand down a ruling declaring the Constitution to be no rigid document, but an elastic one which could cover such actions.

Politics, it will be eternally noted, makes strange bedfellows. The two strong men who stared one another down at the Inauguration of 1801 in fact joined hands to turn the coastal strip called the United States of America into a nation of continental proportions.

THE BLADENSBURG RACES

The lowest point in the new nation's fortunes had been the cruel war winter of 1777–78 at Valley Forge. But at least that episode possessed dignity. Now we come to a low point that had none. It occurred in the time of the fourth President, who succeeded Jefferson: James Madison.

Madison was short and bald, and made speeches as though he were musing to himself. He was brilliant and very well educated. When the young states of Maryland and Virginia held a conference on the navigation of their joint river, the Potomac, and other problems, he turned the meeting into the Congress that produced our Constitution in 1789. He directed that Congress until it created the United States of America, then he led the writing of *The Federalist* papers to persuade the people to agree to it. He is justly called the father of the Constitution.

Above: Dolly Madison.

Of his enormous list of achievements, an outstanding one was that of persuading Mrs. Dolly Payne Todd, a widow, to marry him. She was rosy-cheeked, round and kind and lively; she supports the generalization that our first ladies have often been nicer people than our first men. Dolly Madison may have been the nicest of all first ladies, though the competition is great. Her stucco home still exists on Lafayette Square.

At this time one of the great rivalries of world history—the struggle between Napoleon and the British—was approaching a climax. In trying to strangle each other, they mistreated American ships and sailors badly, and America in 1812 went to war with the British.

Below: her satin dress, embroidered with insects and flowers of North America.

While fighting in Canada, Americans burned down the town of York (later to be renamed Toronto). In the fall of 1814, the British sent a fleet along the American coast to take revenge.

To protect Washington, fortifications were built at the southernmost tip of the city on Greenleaf Point. There fires were kept burning to make cannonballs red-hot before hurling them at any enemy ships coming up the Potomac.

But the British did not come that way; they went to the next river above the Potomac, the Patuxent, and unloaded 4,500 veterans of the Napoleonic wars. These troops approached the capital city from the north. At the crossroads of Bladensburg, Maryland, they sent the American militia running. The poor American performance was ridiculed by nicknaming the battle "the Bladensburg Races."

President Madison drove to the scene in his carriage, carrying two borrowed dueling pistols. Meanwhile, Mrs. Madison was packing the full-length portrait of George Washington (which is the only object, present in the White House the day it opened, which is still there today) and preparing to flee. Trains of wagons left the federal city loaded down with official documents.

The British moved into the emptied city without meeting further resistance and proceeded to burn public buildings, including the White House and the Capitol. The only private homes they burned were two houses said to have been built as an investment by George Washington. Dr. William Thornton, designer of the Capitol, persuaded the British not to burn the Patent Office on the grounds that its technological records were the property of civilization.

The British lost more men in Washington than did the fleet-footed Americans. An ammunition explosion, a violent thunderstorm, and a more violent windstorm, which blew bricks down upon them, took a high toll.

The British boarded their ships and went to Baltimore to try to repeat their success. That city, guarded by Fort McHenry, proved to be better defended, and the British were turned away. Francis Scott Key, a lawyer from the District of Columbia, happened to be a temporary British prisoner. In the light of the "rockets' red glare" he watched the assault on the American fort from a British ship.

The burning of Washington, as shown in a picture published a few months later.

The successful resistance of Fort McHenry inspired him to compose "The Star-Spangled Banner." The huge flag which waved defiantly through the night is now a prized exhibit in the Smithsonian Institution in Washington.

Following the British raid, the White House was little more than a shell.

SECOND CHANCE

"I do not suppose the government will ever return to Washington," wrote a leading citizeness. "All those whose property is invested in that place will be reduced to poverty."

On the charred ruins of the Capitol bitter citizens chalked the words, "The Capital and the Union Lost by Cowardice."

The diplomatic corps at that time consisted of representatives of five nations. Of them, Spain had never set up its offices in the wilderness city. Now the four others quit the city in favor of pleasanter towns.

Madison's flight from Washington, as imagined by a cartoonist.

The President returned and took up residence in the little Octagon House (which today is the headquarters of the American Institute of Architects). Congress returned too, but the sentiment in favor of moving the capital elsewhere was strong. Sensing opportunity, the Pennsylvania towns of Philadelphia and Lancaster offered sites for a new federal city. Of Washington a visitor said, "The appearance of our public buildings is enough to make one cut his throat. The dissolution of the Union is the theme of almost every private conversation."

For weeks Congress debated whether to move. But then the tide turned back in favor of keeping the capital where it was. Two developments did much to solidify this view. A group of Washington citizens pooled resources and began building a temporary Capitol of brick across from the ruins, on the spot where the Supreme Court building is located today. Even more persuasive was the news from New Orleans four months earlier. When British forces sought to invade that city, they ran smack into a polyglot army commanded by a tornado on horseback named General Andrew Jackson. Jackson lost 13 men. The British lost 1,971 men and the battle. National pride revived. Congress voted to rebuild Washington.

"The destruction of Washington," wrote the historians Morison and Commager, "only showed that invading a country like the United States is like hurling a hammer into a bin of corn. A few kernels were hurt, but the hammer had to be withdrawn quickly or lost."

For the city of Washington the decision to rebuild was a milestone. The prospect of moving the capital to another city would be discussed from time to time, but never again so seriously considered.

After the burning of the White House, President Madison and his wife lived in the small house later known as Octagon House (today the headquarters of the American Institute of Architects).

CHAPTER THREE
A CONTEMPTIBLE HAMLET

This embryo capital, where Fancy sees
Squares in morasses, obelisks in trees.
                        —Thomas Moore (1804)

The choice, L'Enfant wrote in a letter, lay between making Washington "a splendid inviting capital" or a "mere contemptible hamlet." For its first half-century it was more nearly the latter.

An English visitor who rode into town in its early years found it so wild that he "travelled a good way into the city before I saw it." Of the one hundred or more streets planned by L'Enfant, sections of only three had been cleared when the government arrived. Not until 1820 did the government order farmers to stop fencing in and planting places meant to be streets. Not until near the Civil War were the last tree stumps moved from them.

Oil lamps were set up near the Capitol and the White House. But there was no money for oil, so they became merely ornaments. A stagecoach provided a bus service between Georgetown and Capitol Hill for one year; then it gave up, and riding horseback became the chief means of locomotion. Walking was difficult by day and dangerous by night on streets pocked with holes, stumps, and piles of wood and brick.

Happily it was a law-abiding city, even in darkness. It had but one policeman until 1811, when the force was doubled. The White House remained unguarded and unlocked. In the time of President Jackson, a marauder entered the White House by mistake and fled when he found where he was. Under Jackson's successor, Van Buren, a drunk wandered in and slept on a couch.

No city ever suffered such ebbs and flows of population. When Congress was in session, there was an overflow of hangers-on

Mrs. John Quincy Adams'
dress of white satin
and silver braid.

and job-seekers. The city was an early attraction for paupers, who assumed that the federal government could help them. When Congress left town almost everyone else did too, including the President and the diplomats. The author Washington Irving, visiting the capital in an ebb period, said, "You cannot imagine how forlorn this desert city appears to me now that the great tide of casual population has rolled away."

Quite early, writers saw the possibilities of this unique place for information and gossip. Anne Royall, author of gossipy books, pestered the sixth President, John Quincy Adams (one of whose achievements was to introduce long trousers and end the reign of knee breeches), for an interview. President Adams took a swim in the clear Potomac each day, and one day Anne followed him and sat upon his clothing, keeping the Chief Executive in the water and in the nude for an hour and a half until he consented to the interview.

As the vast new territories crystallized into states, rough Western Congressmen and their followers swarmed to Washington. Congress was filled with loungers, whittlers, and spitters—above all, spitters. "Washington may be called the headquarters of the tobacco-tinctured saliva," wrote the famous English novelist, Charles Dickens, on a visit. "I strongly recommend all strangers not to look at the floor; and if they happen to drop anything, though it be their purse, not to pick it up with an ungloved hand on any account."

Spittoons were characteristic Washington ornaments until World War II. Then they were scrapped to save the labor of polishing them and to provide brass for armaments. The deathbed census revealed that there were 58,000 spittoons in the city's public buildings!

The city began to attract a few wealthy people as permanent inhabitants. The War of 1812, and lesser naval engagements, brought wealth to some officers in the form of prize moneys from captured ships, and a few of them settled in Washington. Commodore David Porter built himself a mansion north of the city on Meridian Hill. That hill got its name when the government drew a line running due north and south from the White House, hoping to displace the famous Greenwich Meridian of London as the place from which to measure all time and distance. It did not succeed. Meridian Hill is a pleasant park today, and the Greenwich Meridian of London remains zero longitude and the central line of the world map.

Commodore Stephen Decatur built a fine house which is still in use on Lafayette Square, in front of the White House and opposite the house to which Dolly Madison moved after her husband's death. Decatur is most famous for a toast he once proposed: "Our country! In her intercourse with foreign nations, may she always be in the right; but our country, right or wrong." He posed the problem of whether country or truth comes first—a question which is still hotly argued.

In March, 1820, the Decatur home was festive for a party in honor of President Monroe's daughter. A week later it was in mourning when the Commodore's body was carried in, following a silly duel at Bladensburg.

Decatur House was designed by Benjamin Latrobe, creator of the "corncob" column tops in the Capitol. He also designed the "Church of the Presidents"—St. John's Episcopal Church—built near Decatur House on Lafayette Square. Off the square but nearer the White House was Blair House, owned by Francis P. Blair, confidant of Presidents from Jackson to Lincoln, and today the place where Presidential guests are housed. Altogether, the White House area was becoming a cluster of lovely buildings.

St. John's Episcopal Church (left) and Blair House (right) were among the lovely buildings erected near the White House by the 1820s.

up nearly a third of the lots in Washington and promised to build houses promptly on many of them. He planned to finance his purchases by borrowing money from the Netherlands. But Napoleon occupied the Netherlands and absorbed all its funds. Greenleaf could not pay and went bankrupt; and Washington lost a potential source of local wealth. That is the economic story of the city's early life. Washington simply lacked the financial muscle to create a commercial center and take advantage of its marvelous short canal.

Of course, the new city should have been provided with funds by the federal government. Most cities live by taxing their businesses. But Washington's only business was government, and the government refused to be taxed. So the city had to pay its expenses from the taxes of a few permanent inhabitants. And the city's local government (mayors began to be elected after 1820) feared putting pressure on the federal government to pay, lest it accept the proposal of cities like St. Louis to move the capital into the heartland of the continent.

As a possible commercial or industrial center, Washington was hopeless. The city had but one thing to sell, and that was national pride. L'Enfant knew that, and made it the basis of his plans. But it was a long time before anyone else came to the same realization.

THE WESTERNER

In the late winter of 1829, Washington was a city of fear. John Randolph of Roanoke said, "The country is ruined past redemption." Senator Daniel Webster wrote home to Boston, "My *fear* is stronger than my *hope*." Margaret Bayard Smith, wife of the city's leading publisher, said that government employees were "tremblingly alive to what may happen," and that there had been suicides and a sharp fall in the value of property. The cause of all this dismay was the election of Andrew Jackson, hero of New Orleans, as seventh President of the United States. He was the first President from the West.

Jackson's newspaper in the capital threatened that the new President would fire anyone who had worked for a past Administration—which was almost everyone in Washington. He was thought to be an enemy of "improvements" paid for by the government, and the city of Washington was in special need of improvement.

As Jackson approached the city a mob of Westerners preceded him—rough, foul-smelling, frightening—the biggest crowd ever packed into the city, come to see their man inaugurated.

Andrew Jackson during his Presidency.

The city was also terrified because Jackson was a terrifying figure. At sixty-two, he bore the marks of a violent life. His head displayed a scar dealt him by a British officer's sword when as a boy he refused to polish the officer's boots. Bullets from two duels were lodged in his lean, muscular body. His face was furrowed into a fierce frown. He was arriving in a city that knew he had a special reason for vengeance: His beloved wife, Rachel, had just died, hastened to her grave by false stories of immorality spread by Jackson's political opponents.

Before the inauguration, Jackson stayed at the National Hotel on Pennsylvania Avenue near the Capitol. At first he offered to receive any citizen who wished to speak with him. The crush within the hotel and for blocks around was so great that he had to give up the attempt.

On Inauguration Day, the old man stalked out of the hotel and marched up Capitol Hill on foot, his uncovered locks looking like whitecapped waves swept apart by a fast ship. He intended to go to the east front entrance. But the crowd was so big and dense that he climbed a wall and entered the basement of the Capitol. After the swearing-in, he mounted a horse and led the cheering throng down Pennsylvania Avenue to the White House, where all were invited in.

An English artist, Robert Cruikshank, portrayed the uproar when President Jackson invited the public to the White House.

Greenough's statue of George Washington.

Next to the burning by the British, this was the mansion's worst ordeal. Curtains were torn down, walls cracked, furniture broken. Jackson himself was pinned to a wall by a sea of admirers. He extricated himself and rode back to his hotel at the first opportunity. The mob was coaxed out of the White House only by the stratagem of moving the punch bowls out to the lawn; then windows and doors were bolted.

Now Jackson was Chief Executive, and the citizens of Washington winced before impending disaster. But it never came. Jackson's men had overstated his fierceness. In eight years in office, he dismissed fewer than one-fifth of the government employees. His fierce manner was in fact an expression of pain from broken health and sorrow at his wife's death. Though in theory opposed to "improvements," he bestowed many of them on the city.

In the time of John Quincy Adams, when a party had overflowed into the East Room of the White House, guests were shocked to find it in the same unplastered condition as when John Quincy's mother, Abigail, hung her washing in it in 1800. Jackson now finished it, and the East Room has ever since been the nation's premier ballroom. Outside, the temporary wooden steps were replaced with the present permanent stone porticoes.

The present big Treasury building was begun next to the White House. Sadly, it obstructs the view down Pennsylvania Avenue which L'Enfant had insisted on. A story has it that Jackson's aides quarreled over a location, so the impatient President drove his walking cane into the ground and ordered the building begun there —where it is today.

More important than any physical improvement, Jackson opposed the doctrine that the states had greater power than the Union. To Washington, center and symbol of the Union, that was his best contribution.

THE NATION'S ATTIC

Now monuments began to blossom in the city. In 1830, Congress voted money to pay a sculptor named Horace Greenough to make a statue of George Washington to grace the rotunda, or round center hall, of the Capitol. Greenough went to Rome, ordered marble from Michelangelo's quarries in Carrara, and spent years chipping and polishing. A ship of especially large tonnage had to be sent to bring the completed statue to America.

The statue was a large seated figure of the first President, bare to the waist, pointing one hand heavenward. Greenough argued that fashions in clothing change, but his half-bare Washington would be eternal. Congress disagreed. After two years in the rotunda, the statue was moved to the park outside, then later deposited in the Smithsonian Institution, where you can see it today.

Since this memorial to the country's father was deemed a failure, private citizens began collecting money to build a different one—a high stone obelisk. In 1848 the cornerstone was laid, and building began on the Mall. In 1855 funds were exhausted, and building stopped until long after the Civil War. The Washington Monument eventually became the tallest masonry structure in the world, but you can see clearly where money once ran out, for a change to stone of a different age leaves a clear mark.

In 1853, the first equestrian statue ever cast in America was set up in Lafayette Square, facing the front door of the White House. It represents Andrew Jackson on a rearing horse, a feat of balance achieved by making the horse's hindquarters of solid bronze from melted cannon. So successful was it that the sculptor, Clark Mills, was promptly commissioned to portray George Washington on horseback. The unveiling of this statue on Washington Circle, toward the Georgetown end of Pennsylvania Avenue, in 1860, was the last bipartisan event in the city before the Civil War.

Before turning to that grim climax, let us mention the birth of a most useful monument. In 1829 an English scientist named James Smithson died in Genoa, Italy. He willed the new nation, which

Clark Mills's equestrian statues of George Washington (left) and Andrew Jackson (right).

he had never seen and which knew nothing of him, half a million dollars, then an enormous sum.

The most probable of several theories explaining his act is this: He was an illegitimate son of the Duke of Northumberland, and was refused the use of his father's name. He was bitter toward the nobility and therefore favorable to the foremost Republic. He once swore that "my name shall live in the memory of man when the titles of the Northumberlands and the Percys are extinct and forgotten." Those names are still well known, but Smithson's chances of outlasting them are good.

In 1852, halfway between Congress and the stump of the Washington Monument, a redstone castle was erected on the Mall, using the bequest. It was called the Smithsonian Institution. It became the nation's fascinating attic, where every precious or interesting object was stored—from George Washington's surveying instruments, Francis Scott Key's star-spangled flag, and the dresses of all our first ladies to the *Kitty Hawk,* the *Spirit of St. Louis,* and the newest astronautical vehicle.

The Smithsonian Institution, photographed in 1862.

It was also a magnificent laboratory and school. To learn how

to stuff dead animals, the Institution acquired a collection of live ones. They became the city's excellent zoo in Rock Creek Park, which is still supervised by the Smithsonian Institution.

Next to the Capitol, Smithson's red castle and its numerous auxiliary buildings in the Mall receive tributes each year from a greater number of admiring visitors than anything else in the city.

BLACK WASHINGTON

From the very first, Negroes have felt a special tie to the federal city. As we have seen, it was laid out in part by a Negro, Benjamin Banneker. There is in the city the oldest Negro aristocracy in the nation, able to trace forbears back beyond what many Daughters of the American Revolution can legitimately claim. Negroes have always constituted a high percentage of the city's population, and Washington is today the only city outside Africa with a Negro majority of residents.

The reasons for its attractiveness to Negroes are easy to find. To begin with, it was a Southern city with an atmosphere familiar to migrants from the South. Then, although conditions cannot honestly be said to have been favorable for Negroes anywhere, they were less unfavorable in Washington than elsewhere. That was because most of the elected members of the federal government, including the early Southern Presidents, opposed slavery and felt an obligation to assist its victims.

Thus, while the education of Negroes was forbidden in most Southern states, Negroes in Washington maintained their own schools in the federal city beginning in 1807. There were economic restrictions on them elsewhere, but in Washington they could earn money, purchase their freedom, and even buy businesses and become well off. In the first eleven years of the nineteenth century, the number of free Negroes in the city multiplied by seven. By the time of the Civil War, there were only 2,000 Negro slaves in the city, in contrast to 9,000 free Negroes.

With the formation of Western territories into states, the competition between slavery and antislavery forces to extend their ways of life became acute. The struggle was reflected in Washington by both trivial and serious incidents, as each side sought to win symbolic successes in the federal city, hoping thereby to improve its chances in the rest of the nation.

Each year until 1835, antislavery Congressmen introduced a bill to abolish slavery in the District of Columbia. Then a growing

In the Smithsonian: dress of Emily Donelson, niece of President Andrew Jackson and First Lady of the White House.

A group of slaves chained together, with the unfinished Capitol in the background.

fear that the issue would tear the Union apart led to a "gag rule" forbidding debate on the subject. But outside Congress in the city the struggle became fiercer. The Abolitionists launched a newspaper, the *National Era,* in Washington. The Southerners countered with a journal called the *Southern Press.*

In 1848 an incident forced the issue into Congress once more. A New England sea captain named Daniel Drayton arranged to smuggle seventy-six domestic slaves out of the city to freedom. His sailing ship full of human cargo fell into a calm at the mouth of the Potomac. Many white families, among them Dolly Madison's household, woke up to find no breakfast waiting. After a brief investigation, police were sent out to the becalmed vessel, where the slaves were found and returned.

Drayton was sentenced to four years in prison. But the resentment of the antislavery forces now broke the gag rule. In a debate in the House of Representatives, a gawky new Congressman from the West announced he would introduce a bill forbidding slavery in the capital city. Eventually his plan was absorbed into the Compromise of 1850. In Washington, the owning of slaves would continue, but the buying and selling of them would be forbidden. The young Congressman stayed in the city only one term, then returned to obscurity. He was from Illinois and his name was Abraham Lincoln.

From the middle 1850s on, the issue became raw. At this time the Capitol was being enlarged, and the symbolic figure of Freedom which would eventually be put atop the new dome arrived in town. Senator Jefferson Davis of Mississippi noted that the figure wore a liberty cap of the kind worn by ancient Roman slaves who had been freed. He called this a provocation of the South. The harassed sculptor substituted feathers for the cap, and from the ground today Mistress Freedom on her high perch looks rather like an Indian with a disheveled war bonnet.

On the floor of the Senate, a Southern Senator took his cane to a Northern Senator and nearly killed him. A Negro girls' school on 19th Street was attacked and set afire by a mob. At Harper's Ferry, up the Potomac Valley, wild-eyed old John Brown and sixteen fanatics seized a federal arsenal with intent to foment and arm a slave rebellion. Colonel Robert E. Lee was sent to subdue and arrest Brown's tiny army. The year was 1859.

The Smithsonian's plaster cast of the figure of Freedom atop the Capitol dome.

That year out in Illinois, the gawky ex-Congressman passed his fiftieth birthday and could well have summed himself up as a political failure. But a year later he was elected President of the United States. His election was the fuse that blew the nation apart. South Carolina did not even bother to send its Congressional delegation back to Washington. Those members of Congress who came divided promptly into pro-Union and anti-Union camps. Only one Southerner favored the Union—Senator Andrew Johnson of Tennessee.

Some public-spirited people under old ex-President John Tyler met for a "peace conference" in Willard's Hotel near the White House, hoping to paper the Union together with talk.

President James Buchanan was so harassed by a nation cracking and splitting and demanding decisions that he cried out, "The office of President of the United States is not fit for a gentleman to hold!" All Southerners and many Northerners could accept that judgment on the grounds that the next holder of the office—now on his slow special train from Illinois to Washington—was no gentleman.

CHAPTER FOUR
THE CITADEL: 1860-1865

A CAPTAIN FOR THE STORM

Americans and non-Americans are in remarkable agreement about the identity of the greatest man ever to live in Washington. Eighty American historians placed his name at the top of a list published in *The New York Times* a few years ago. About the same time, at the World's Fair in Brussels, an American voting machine was displayed. By pulling a lever, foreign visitors could vote for whomever they considered the greatest American. Almost all chose the same figure.

Yet this man made his entrance into Washington in a manner so lacking in dignity that it pained him ever afterward to remember the episode.

It was February 23, 1861. At six in the morning the regular train from Baltimore arrived at the depot near the foot of Capitol Hill, and passengers swarmed off it. Almost no one noticed a curious trio in the crowd. A very short man and a very broad man walked on either side of a very tall man wearing a soft wool hat. At the end of the platform, Congressman Elihu Washburne of Illinois stood by a column studying faces. When he saw the tall central figure, he stepped out and said, "Abe, you can't play that on me!"

Thus Abraham Lincoln, about to be inaugurated as sixteenth President of the United States, arrived at history's center stage. Unwillingly, he had allowed himself to be persuaded that there was a plot to assassinate him. He had secretly left his special train and come ahead with two bodyguards on the regular train from Baltimore, nine hours before he was expected.

At this moment, it would have taken special insight to see greatness in this outlandish figure. Lincoln had devoted his life to

Lincoln shown sneaking into Washington in a freight car—one of many derogatory cartoons about the newly elected President.

Abraham Lincoln (photograph by Mathew Brady, leading photographer of the Civil War).

politics, but had lost more often than he had won. Only because of a split in the party opposing him had he won the Presidency—with fewer than half the votes cast.

His eleven-day train journey to the capital had been marked by poor speeches. In Columbus, Ohio, he had expressed satisfaction that so far "there is nothing going wrong." With six states already having left the Union and more threatening to do so, this seemed a stupid comment.

The famous Boston orator, Edward Everett, wrote in his diary, "He is evidently a person of very inferior cast of character, wholly unequal to the crisis." The New York *Herald* said he had "no capacity to grapple manfully with the dangers of this crisis."

We do not know exactly how he looked, for when he was being photographed he froze his features. Actually, he grinned much of the time and was given to joking and to twangy mispronunciations of words. At this crucial point in history, he struck observers as being silly. The Salem *Advocate* wrote, "He is no more capable of being a statesman . . . than the braying ass can become a noble lion."

When to his bad speeches, his curious rawboned appearance, and his joking way you add his undignified arrival by sneaking into town, you can understand the nearly disastrous impression Lincoln made.

In the South at this time there were defiance and high spirit. The North was gloomy. Northerners felt that they were getting inferior leadership. They assumed that the President-elect did not know what to do and in any case lacked courage to do it. But in truth there was no other way for Lincoln to behave. He was not yet President. He sought to avoid a warlike manner in the hope that the South might drift back into the Union. In fact, there was rarely a more resolute President-elect. He was absolutely determined not to let the Union be dissolved and not to let slavery be extended.

After the inauguration—on a dingy day beneath the domeless new Capitol—commissioners from the South came to ask that the remaining federal forts and property in the South be surrendered. Lincoln's Secretary of State, William Seward, assured them that Lincoln would hand over the federal property, including Fort Sumter in the bay of Charleston, South Carolina. The General in Chief of the Union, old General Winfield Scott, advised Lincoln to give up Sumter. It was one of those times when most of Lincoln's advisers voted Aye and Lincoln voted Nay, so the Nays had it. Lincoln ordered that Sumter be supplied. Confederate guns fired on the fort until it surrendered, and the Civil War began.

In Washington, the next week was one of panic not equaled before or since. Virginia quit the Union and her troops seized Alexandria. From the White House, Lincoln could see a Confederate flag flying there. The city was thus cut off from the South. Confederates seized Harper's Ferry on the upper Potomac, cutting the city off from the West. Mobs in Baltimore burned railroads and destroyed telegraph lines, cutting the city off from the North. And as the banks of the lower Potomac were within range of Virginia guns, the city was cut off from the East—and was, in sum, isolated from the world.

Said General Scott, "They are closing their coils around us." He laid plans to hold the Capitol and the White House area against a Southern invasion. Because shells containing sawdust instead of explosive were found in the Navy Yard, he suspected treason within the city.

For four terrible days the city was isolated. The town emptied as people fled. Then troops from New York, Massachusetts, and Pennsylvania arrived over railway lines that were repaired and

Arrival in Washington of New York's Seventy-first Regiment, May 1861.

guarded. More Northern troops followed. The Confederates abandoned both Alexandria and Harper's Ferry. The panic ended.

Lincoln moved decisively, assuming powers that normally would have been considered tyrannical. Without waiting for Congress he called for volunteers. He added ten regiments to the Army and 18,000 men to the Navy. He proclaimed a blockade of the South's coast from Virginia down to Texas. He suspended the constitutional right of *habeas corpus* in order to permit arrest without stating cause anywhere along the railroad from New York to Washington. He also called a special session of Congress to confirm all these decisions.

Within his cabinet, it had been assumed that the real ruler of the nation would be Secretary of State William Seward. A memorandum indicating this assumption was drafted by Seward and given to Lincoln. The President responded politely but firmly, banishing the thought. Within a year Seward would write to his wife, "The President is the best of us." It would take a little longer, but Edward Everett and the New York *Herald* would agree. So would the Union and, eventually, many of those in rebellion against it.

WHAT MIGHT HAVE BEEN

Perhaps the finest view of Washington may be had from Arlington Heights on the Virginia side of the Potomac. From there today you

A recruiting poster for the Union Army.

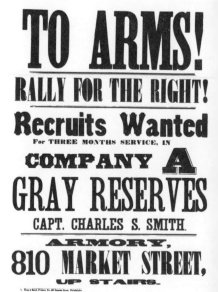

TO ARMS!
RALLY FOR THE RIGHT!
Recruits Wanted
For THREE MONTHS SERVICE, IN
COMPANY A
GRAY RESERVES
CAPT. CHARLES S. SMITH.
ARMORY,
810 MARKET STREET,
UP STAIRS.

can see directly before you the tomb of L'Enfant, and a little below it on the same slope the grave of John F. Kennedy. Beyond that across the river the Lincoln Memorial, the Washington Monument, and the Capitol are almost in a straight line.

On the hill from which this view is to be had stands Arlington House—formerly called the Custis-Lee Mansion—a plantation mansion with a portico of unusually thick Doric columns. At night the portico is lighted, and in the darkness on its hill it looks from a distance like a toy house hanging in the Virginia sky. The house was built by George Washington's stepson the year the federal government moved to Washington. It was inherited by his daughter, who married young Robert Edward Lee. In this pleasant old home, Colonel Lee made one of those rare personal decisions that have altered American history.

Lee was the favorite subordinate of General Winfield Scott. When the first states seceded, Scott sent for Lee, who had been assigned to Texas after quelling John Brown's rebellion. Scott received Lee in his headquarters, the Winder Building on 17th Street (an edifice unchanged today except that it is now the office which administers aid in national disasters). Scott offered Lee the command of the Union Army, then being formed. What Lee answered is not known. He returned to Arlington House, where he stayed the following month.

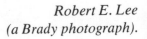

Robert E. Lee (a Brady photograph).

Then Lee was asked to return to the city by a prominent news-paper editor, Francis P. Blair. Lee went to Blair House, where he was urged in the name of President Lincoln to accept the offer. This time Lee was definite. As he recalled it, he said that "though opposed to secession and deprecating war, I could take no part in an invasion of the Southern states." That evening he crossed the bridge to his home for the last time.

In the war that followed, all the advantages seemed to be on one side: The North had eighteen and a half million people from which to draw soldiers and workers. The South had half that number. The North had over one million workers involved in manufacturing. The South had one-tenth that number. In amounts of bank deposits —a rough measure of the capital available to finance a war—the North had four times as much as the South. The North had twenty million miles of railroads with which to move men and goods, against the South's nine million miles.

As the red-haired Northerner, William Tecumseh Sherman, told a Louisiana friend, "The North can make a steam engine, loco-motive, or railway car; hardly a yard of cloth or a pair of shoes can you make. You are rushing into war with one of the most powerful, ingeniously mechanical, and determined people on earth—right at your doors. You are bound to lose."

The North had everything—except military commanders.

Most of the officers of the U.S. Army at that time were South-erners. Of the six departments into which the Army was divided, five were commanded by Southerners. Because Southerners con-trolled promotions, Northern officers tended to drift away to seek careers in other fields. When the Civil War began there were 700 officers in the U.S. Army. More than 300 resigned and went south immediately. Of those that remained, only two had ever commanded a unit as large as a brigade.

Throughout the Civil War, the main theater of conflict was around Washington. In that decisive area the history of the war was the story of great Northern numbers, commanded by hesitant and timid commanders, against smaller Southern numbers, com-manded by military geniuses—of whom Lee was foremost.

In the final year of war, Lincoln found the right general to command the Northern forces. But had Lee joined him in the begin-ning, the war might have been shorter and might not have injected deep bitterness into American life for a century afterward.

Lee wrote his sister in Baltimore, "With all my devotion to the Union and the feeling of loyalty and duty as an American citizen,

I have not been able to make up my mind to raise my hand against my relatives, my children, my home."

There was something tragically appropriate in the conversion of Arlington plantation into a great national cemetery in the final year of the war. On the rolling hills where the young officer once planted crops now appear orderly rows of white gravestones, bearing names of Americans who died on both sides in the Civil War, as well as others who died on America's side in later wars.

A VILLAGE DOES A CITY'S WORK

No city ever grew as fast as Washington did after the first panic ended. In the first quarter-century of its existence, its population increased at a rate of 500 new inhabitants per year. After the Civil War began, it grew at a rate of 500 new inhabitants per *day*.

The postmaster of the Washington area said that when he took up his duties in 1860, he was delivering mail to 60,000 people. By the last year of the war he was delivering mail to 1,000,000 people. These included a great number of temporary residents, such as soldiers in camps and the wounded in hospitals.

Washington assumed new importance and attracted all these people for three reasons: The city was located at the battlefront, between the warring sides. So inevitably it became the largest camp and hospital and supply depot for the biggest army that had ever existed in the Western Hemisphere. The city was where decisions were made, contracts granted to industry, money appropriated, and citizens ordered to risk life and property—so tens of thousands of people poured in to try to influence these decisions. Finally, the city was a symbol of immense value. Because it was the citadel of the Union, if the South could capture it the North would be greatly demoralized. So troops were packed in and around Washington to prevent its capture.

Troops were lodged wherever a roof existed, including the East Ballroom of the White House and every room in the Capitol. The Capitol basement became a giant bakery, so that building enjoyed one of the few pleasant odors in the city. The Foggy Bottom region, between the White House and Georgetown, was made into a corral where at one time 30,000 horses were kept, fed, and shod. The grounds of the Washington Monument became a tremendous slaughterhouse, which provided meat for all the troops and contributed an additional unpleasant odor to that of the increasingly mucky Tiber canal. The green banks of the Potomac were now cut

into and lined with long strings of wharves, for most supplies soon came by water.

Though labor was in demand for war purposes, Lincoln ordered a continuation of the two largest building projects begun before the war. One was the building of the enlarged Capitol. Work on this, Lincoln felt, would be interpreted as confidence in the continuance of the Union. The other was a great project to pipe Potomac water from above Great Falls, north of the city, down into Washington. The old springs of the city, which supplied plenty of water for a village, could not meet the demands of one of the most populous cities in the world.

L'Enfant had planned 270 miles of streets in the center of the city. In 1860 most had no houses on them. Now all were soon lined with houses, and behind 55 miles of them, shacks were built in alleys which became among the worst slums in America. A few of these alley slums are still there.

Where people and money accumulated, crime followed. The tiny Washington police force was absorbed into a new metropolitan force numbering 160 men. In addition, the Provost Marshal created a military police of 1,000 men. In a single year of the war, the police made 24,000 arrests in Washington. That was three and a half times as many as were made in Brooklyn the same year, though Brooklyn had double the population of central Washington.

The city could not adapt itself to the flash flood of humanity. The traffic of heavily laden army wagons and of troops with heavy

Massachusetts troops had to be quartered in the roofless rotunda of the Capitol. Thornton's original low dome (see page 21) was being replaced with the present high dome.

Mrs. Lincoln's dress of purple velvet trimmed with silk and lace.

equipment broke the backs of the thinly paved avenues, turning them into trenches of mud or channels of choking dust. Primitive sanitary facilities broke down, and the Tiber canal was simply turned into the world's biggest open sewer. Dredging it to keep it deep enough for navigation became impossible, and it turned into a soup of "decaying animal or vegetable matter."

Typhoid, dysentery, and above all scarlet fever became the city's scourges. The President himself was stricken with a mild case of smallpox, and his son Willie died of typhoid fever. The blow nearly broke the already overburdened mind of Mrs. Lincoln.

Illness and wounds turned the city into the biggest hospital center ever known. Washington had one hospital when the war began; it shortly had thirty-six. Following particularly bloody battles, its hospital population rose to 50,000, more than the city's total population ten years before the war.

With all its miseries, Washington was also a lively place. The city which had had trouble filling one theater now filled four. One of them was a Baptist church converted into a theater by John T. Ford. President Lincoln went there twice to watch a handsome young actor, John Wilkes Booth.

A layer of very wealthy people appeared at the top of society, with a thicker layer of fairly wealthy ones just below. An author noted that if Washington could not win the war, it was at least proving it could make money out of it. Some people went to four or five parties an evening. A summit of luxury was reached at the second Inaugural Ball, where sixty-five different dishes were served.

Among the pastimes was a new game called Base Ball. It was played on diamonds located on the grounds south of the White House. As the game is still played there, that is probably the oldest ball field in use in America.

The uncomfortable village had always been a masculine place, for few office-holders and visitors would subject their wives to it. Now in wartime women were needed, and they enriched the life of the city immeasurably. Clara Barton, a shy employee of the government, began her pioneer work of bringing aid and relief to troops. A young girl from New England volunteered as a nurse and suffered the usual crisis at seeing bloody wounds; afterward Louisa May Alcott returned home and wrote *Little Women*. Julia Ward Howe, haunted by the soldiers' sad songs, sat up one night in Willard's Hotel and composed the lines to be known as the "Battle Hymn of the Republic." And there is the story of Lincoln's bending down to take the hand of a frail visitor and saying, "So you are the

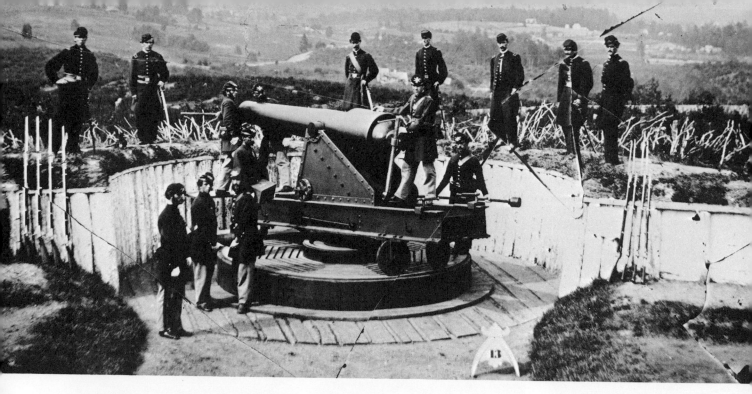

little woman who started the war!" She was Harriet Beecher Stowe, author of *Uncle Tom's Cabin*.

From many elements, the "contemptible hamlet" was fusing a special and rather strong new spirit of its own. One dark night two women walked beneath the unfinished dome of the Capitol. They regarded it in silence, then one said to the other, "I wonder if it will ever be finished?" From the shadows a sentry moved forward and said in a clear firm voice, "Yes, ma'am!"

THE WAR FOR WASHINGTON

Of all the theaters of the war, the one where success would mean victory, and failure would mean defeat, was Washington. For four terrible years the Army of the Potomac for the North and the Army of Northern Virginia for the South fought a duel that poured more American blood into the soil in front of, behind, and beside the nation's capital than has been shed anywhere else at any time.

First Bull Run

The baptism by blood took place on a fine July day in 1861. Union troops marched out of Washington to the Manassas railroad junction, twenty-five miles southward. They aimed to drive away a Southern force there and use the junction for an advance on Richmond, Virginia, the Confederate capital.

It is a mark of how ill prepared they were that their commanding general could not find a usable map of Virginia for the march.

Fort Totten, one of many forts established within the District of Columbia.

Advertisement of about 1860 for Uncle Tom's Cabin. *Published eight years earlier, the book aroused strong Northern feelings against slavery.*

135,000 SETS, 270,000 VOLUMES SOLD.

UNCLE TOM'S CABIN

FOR SALE HERE.

AN EDITION FOR THE MILLION, COMPLETE IN 1 Vol. PRICE 37 1-2 CENTS.
" " IN GERMAN, IN 1 Vol. PRICE 50 CENTS.
" . " IN 2 Vols. CLOTH, 6 PLATES, PRICE $1.50.
SUPERB ILLUSTRATED EDITION, IN 1 Vol. WITH 153 ENGRAVINGS.
PRICES FROM $2.50 TO $5.00.

The Greatest Book of the Age.

Southern volunteers, photographed in Richmond before First Bull Run.

Southern forces opposing him were luckier. They received a detailed map, with the Northerners' planned route marked in red pencil, a week before the battle. It was sent by Mrs. Rose Greenhow, who thus launched a spectacular career as a spy from her home facing the White House.

The Union march south was gay. Troops in every kind and color of uniform paused at will to rest. A young soldier wrote in his diary, "Nothing men can do—except picnics with ladies in straw hats with feathers—is so picturesque as soldiering." Carriages full of Washingtonians followed the troops to lay out lunches and watch the battle along Bull Run river.

The clash of arms was violent, but Union troops held their own —until they backed off to regroup and found the roads choked with picnickers rushing home. Panic broke out, and the troops burst into flight. Through the day and night soldiers poured back in the rain to Washington, angry, tired, and beaten.

The poet Walt Whitman, working in the city as a male nurse, called this "the day of Lincoln's Crucifixion." But there were to be much worse crucifixions.

McClellan

It was clear that the troops were not trained to move with speed and to fight. It was also clear that Washington was perilously naked of defense. To meet both situations, Lincoln called General George B. McClellan from a successful foray in the West to take over the Army of the Potomac.

For months after that the frequent sight of General McClellan, galloping through the streets of Washington at any hour of day or night with his retinue strung out behind him, was a heartening vision. McClellan was a natural executive. He built and staffed a ring of strong forts around the city. He policed the city to keep streets clear and idlers out. He drilled and trained soldiers in mass movements at high speed. Soon he had a trained and tough army of 200,000 men in and around Washington.

Alas, McClellan had faults as big as his virtues. He was a supreme egotist who considered himself a divinely appointed savior. He was soon nicknamed "McNapoleon." He accepted no orders or advice. And he was cautious, or downright timid, in using the marvelous army he had created. The President and Congress urged him to move southward and fight. He always produced evidence—false in every case, it turned out—that the enemy had superior forces. When the Confederates finally quit Manassas of

One of the wooden "cannon" that deterred McClellan from attacking Southern troops near Washington.

General George B. McClellan

Confederate dead at Fredericksburg, Virginia.

their own will, it was found that the menacing guns McClellan had feared to assault were in fact merely wooden logs painted black!

After much urging he finally moved south by water and sought to take Richmond by a march inland. At every encounter much smaller forces—commanded by Robert E. Lee after his superior was wounded—outbluffed, outmaneuvered and outfought McClellan, until the campaign was cancelled, and McClellan was called back to Washington.

The Sea Monster

On a Sunday morning in March, 1862, Washington heard terrifying news. A seagoing monster in the service of the Confederacy had appeared in Chesapeake Bay. It was the old U.S. frigate, the *Merrimac,* with a new skin of iron plate four inches thick. Union ships were powerless. Their shots bounced off it, and it then rammed and sank them.

The Cabinet met in emergency session. It considered sinking sixty barges in the Potomac to block the monster's passage to Washington. Northern shipbuilders, however, had had the same idea of armor plating. On the *Merrimac's* next sortie, it ran into the "Cheese-box on a Raft," the U.S.S. *Monitor,* which was equally thickskinned and had a revolving gun turret. The ships fought a two-hour stand-off before the Southern ship made for home. Later its crew blew it up to prevent its capture.

The Habit of Failure

The series of battles for Washington continued, all with one theme: Union power versus Southern skill. Skill prevailed.

In the Second Battle of Bull Run, Lee moved so swiftly that he made fewer troops seem to be more. He beat the Union again. He then crossed the Potomac northward to approach Washington from the rear. At Sharpsburg, Maryland, near the creek which gave the battle its name of Antietam, he fought the bloodiest single fight of the war. Both sides were hurt badly. With a smaller force, Lee was in greater danger at the end. However, Northern troops failed to follow up with a second attack, so he returned safely southward.

A series of Union commanders—Halleck, Burnside, Hooker— failed in a series of bloody encounters. The Army of the Potomac was then entrusted to General George Meade, its fifth commander in a single year. Meade fought what many think was the climactic battle. Lee crossed the Potomac northward again. Meade followed him to Gettysburg, Pennsylvania, and fought him to a draw. But again the North failed to strike a fatal follow-up blow, and Lee's small forces escaped once more.

General Ulysses S. Grant (a Brady photograph).

A dreadfully disappointed Lincoln had been keeping an eye on a general in the West who had been drawing a noose around the Confederacy. The President now sent for this man.

THE RED ROAD TO RICHMOND

One evening early in 1864, a reception was held at the White House. Here is the historian Margaret Leech's description of an incident that evening:

"Near the door of the Blue Room the advance of the column of callers was suddenly checked. The President, after cordially wringing the hand of one visitor, detained him in conversation. He was a short, scrubby officer, stooped and sunburned, with rough, light-brown whiskers, and he appeared scarcely worthy of signal attention. There was something seedy about him; the look of a man who is out of a job, and takes too much to drink. The stars on his shoulder straps were tarnished. But a buzz ran through the Blue Room. Everyone began to stare at the man who stood awkwardly looking up at the President, while arriving guests jostled in confusion outside the doorway."

In an age without newspaper photographs, whispers had to relay

*"Long Abe Lincoln
a Little Longer,"
an 1864 cartoon on
the President's re-election
for a second term.*

through the crowd the news that this was General Ulysses S. Grant, meeting his Commander in Chief for the first time.

Grant seemed to have been marked by life for mediocrity and failure. He was without intellect or vision, and had none of the drive or managerial ability needed for commercial success. He was shy and uncomfortable when being looked at. He had, however, one ability to a degree that amounted virtually to genius. He was a canny and unrelenting fighter. He assumed victory to be the purpose of battle and continued to fight until the purpose was achieved. If one approach did not work, he tried another. If an opponent hit him a blow, he dealt the opponent two blows. After a battle he did not stop to lick wounds, but proceeded to destroy the opponent. These were qualities the capital had seen up until now only in Southern commanders.

At a dark moment in the Union's fortunes, he had smashed his way to Fort Donelson in Tennessee. When the opposing general asked for terms, Grant thrilled the North with the brief message, "No terms except unconditional and immediate surrender can be accepted. I propose to move immediately upon your works."

After a momentary failure, Grant's critics asked that he be removed. Lincoln answered, "I cannot spare this man—he fights." When there were complaints about Grant's drinking, Lincoln said he would make a note of the brand Grant drank and supply his other generals with some of it.

Now Lincoln had called Grant from the West, placed him in command, and given him the rank of Lieutenant General, held hitherto only by George Washington and Winfield Scott.

Grant's advance to Richmond carried the war beyond the city of Washington. Let us only record that it was a bloody mutual bludgeoning by Grant and Lee, and it filled Washington with Confederate prisoners, for Grant discontinued the previous practice of exchanging captives.

At one point the war returned to Washington. Hard-pressed Lee sought relief by sending his cavalry under General Jubal Early over the Potomac northwest of the city and right down into the capital, in the deepest penetration of the war. Washingtonians were now inured to panic. They turned out in thousands to see the invasion. The President watched from a parapet at Fort Stevens (still there on 13th Street in the northern part of the city). A physician standing near him was killed by a sniper's bullet. A young officer shouted to Lincoln, "Get down, you fool!" Lincoln got down. The young officer was Oliver Wendell Holmes, who would one day be a Justice of the Supreme Court. The rebel intrusion came to nothing, because Early promptly withdrew.

Late one night, in the little War Department House next to the White House, a drowsing telegraph operator heard the keys clicking. He did not wait to hear the message, for the first two words were, "From Richmond . . ." With only that, he rushed to shout the news that the Confederate capital had been taken by Grant. Word spread like a prairie fire in a high wind. The city illuminated like a shell-burst as candles and gaslights were lit in every shopwindow and home. Guns of triumph shattered an atmosphere growing loud with people cheering and singing in the streets.

A little later Lee surrendered. In Washington, the man who had offered Lee command of the Union Army nearly four years earlier now walked around the White House in a kind of aged shuffle. He was bent and hollow-eyed from the distress of making too many decisions to shovel too many lives into the furnace of war. On the White House grounds a band played, and the crowd called for Lincoln. Finally he appeared at a window. The bandleader asked what air they might serenade him with. He answered, "Dixie."

White House visitors during the Civil War.

THE HARD ROAD FROM SERFDOM

The Union was fighting to keep the nation whole. Lincoln stated that goal, and the troops behaved accordingly. They were indifferent to the issue of slavery.

But slavery was outdated and discredited. Even in good times it is doubtful that it paid its way. The federal government always refused to use slave labor on public buildings, because more was achieved at less cost by using free workers.

The stress of war now caused the institution to begin breaking up. Northern armies liberated slaves just to deprive the South of labor. The South eventually began putting Negroes into the army, which made it nearly impossible to return them to servitude. And many Negroes simply pulled up roots and followed Union armies, going nowhere except away from slavery. Said General Sherman after a raid in Mississippi, "We bring in some 500 prisoners, a good many refugees, and about ten miles of Negroes!"

Washington became the nation's testing ground for trying out methods of liberation before applying them to the whole country. Slavery was legally ended there six months before the Emancipation Proclamation ended it in most states. The Black Code of laws to keep Negroes in an inferior position was abolished in Washing-

Negro infantry at Fort Lincoln, near Washington.

ton first, then in the nation. Recruitment of Negroes into the Army was tried in Washington, then done generally.

Improvements like these in a city wholly surrounded by slave states resulted in a great influx of escaping slaves. Within six months after slavery was abolished in Washington, the number of escaped slaves there multiplied by ten. By the end of the war, the number in the city was 40,000. The city lacked the resources to help them all. A few model villages were set up on the outskirts of town. But most escaped slaves packed themselves into existing alley slums, or built new and worse slums of driftwood and tar paper along the sickening banks of the Tiber canal.

As legal shackles were removed from Negroes, whites chained them with something new: white prejudice and fear. Mobs of hoodlums attacked Negroes. The operators of the new horse-drawn bus service refused to let Negroes into cars until Congress threatened to revoke the company's charter. The first Negro army recruits had to be moved to the isolation of Analostan Island (now Theodore Roosevelt Island) off Georgetown to keep whites, terrified at seeing Negroes with guns, from assaulting them at night.

After two centuries of shameful enslaving, now began a century of shameful behavior of another sort. In defense of Washington, it should be said that the problem was bigger there than anywhere else, and the city, unable to tax its chief occupant, the government, had fewer resources with which to meet the problem.

What was needed was a thoughtful national program of, say, twenty years of preparation of these illiterate people for full citizenship. What was also needed was an attitude of brotherhood.

MURDER ON TENTH STREET

It is remarkable how little serious thought was given to the possibility that violence might be done to the President. The time was one of extreme passions, and Washington was jammed with oddly assorted people with a variety of grudges. But people then were simply not accustomed to the thought of assassination, and the President was therefore poorly protected.

Up to that time, only two Presidents had died in office, and they died of natural causes. The ninth President, William Henry Harrison (called "Tippecanoe" after an Indian battle fought at a river of that name), had caught pneumonia after reading the longest inaugural speech ever in the freezing rain outside the Capitol. The twelfth President, Zachary Taylor, had died of gastroenteritis after eating too much fresh fruit and drinking too much cold water following a hot July ceremony at the Washington Monument grounds.

Of all the Presidents, only Andrew Jackson had been the target of an assassin. A madman shot at him twice on the spot in the Capitol rotunda where Jackson's bronze statue now stands. But it was well known that Jackson could not be killed, and he was not.

One of the few people who thought Lincoln would die a violent death was Abraham Lincoln. In the last year of the war he recounted a dream: He had walked into the East Room of the White House and seen a coffin lying there. He asked who was inside it. The answer came, "The President."

On two occasions Lincoln had been to see his future assailant, in the theater. On two known occasions the assailant had been to see him. Once he stood outside the White House when Lincoln appeared at a window to be serenaded. And he was present at Lincoln's second inauguration. A famous photograph shows him in the crowd on the Capitol steps just above the President, with his fellow conspirators in a group in the crowd just below the President.

John Wilkes Booth was one of a family of famous actors. He was handsome, spoiled, and unstable. He was theatrically attached to the Southern cause. In the last months of the war, Lee was suffering a shortage of manpower. Booth planned not to kill but to kidnap the President, then offer him back to the Union in return

John Wilkes Booth

Mathew Brady photograph of the second inauguration, showing Lincoln giving his address at a small white table (center).

Lewis Payne, who stabbed Secretary Seward.

for the release of Southern prisoners. To carry out his plan he attracted an odd gang of henchmen about him. The deed was rehearsed in hotel rooms, with Booth wearing glittering military attire and clearly thinking how he would look rather than what he would do.

When the war ended, the plan lost its point. Instead, Booth now planned to assassinate Lincoln and have his fellows kill other Union leaders. He rented the Presidential box at Ford's Theater three times to study its layout.

Little more than a month after the second inauguration, Mrs. Lincoln sought to organize a theater party. General Grant was in town, and Lincoln agreed to the party in order to be able to invite the General and his wife.

Grant unwillingly half-agreed. Then the last day he withdrew. The President was advised to stay home out of the crowds in this excited, end-of-war period. But the President knew that his presence had been advertised, and he disliked disappointing a public he had demanded so much of. Also, he remembered his undignified entrance into Washington four years before, when warned of similar risks, and he was resolved not to suffer such humiliation again. So the Lincolns invited a young army major and his fiancée in place of the Grants, and went to Ford's. Nobody noticed that a small peephole had been freshly drilled in the door to the Presidential box.

Samuel Arnold

Michael O'Laughlin

Edward Spangler

At 10:00 that night, a conspirator entered the home of Secretary of State Seward, stabbed him but failed to kill him, and then fled on horseback. About the same time, Booth silently entered the President's box and fired his little derringer pistol in the back of Lincoln's head.

Booth leaped from the box down to the stage, catching his spur in a flag on the box and breaking his leg. He shouted the motto of Virginia, *Sic Semper Tyrannis* (Thus Always to Tyrants), and limped outside to mount a waiting horse and flee eastward out of the city, then southward into Virginia.

Lincoln was moved to a small house across the street. He never regained consciousness. He died a little after 7:00 the next morning.

Booth had been recognized by many people in the audience, and a pitiless search for him was begun. He was caught in a barn in Virginia and shot, against orders. The other conspirators, and some merely suspected of being such, were rounded up and thrown into

Above: three of the men arrested as members of the Booth conspiracy but not condemned to death.

Below: Lewis Payne and these three people were hanged as members of the Booth conspiracy.

David E. Herold

George A. Atzerodt

Mary Surratt

Lincoln's coffin lying in state in the White House.

the old federal prison at Greenleaf Point. They were chained and hooded, then tried and sentenced. Four were hanged. There on Greenleaf Point—where John Greenleaf had gone bankrupt trying to manipulate Washington real estate, where thirty British invaders had been killed in an explosion in 1814—Booth and four conspirators were buried. Part of the old prison is still there as a barracks, but most of it has been demolished, and the bodies have all been removed.

Lincoln's body lay in state in the White House, and was then moved to the Capitol rotunda in a special ceremony—one which would also be accorded John Kennedy's body a century later. Lincoln's body was then sent on a black-draped train across the nation to Springfield, Illinois, and later buried in an ornate and ugly tomb.

His real monument came half a century later when the Lincoln Memorial was built on land reclaimed from the Potomac. It is one of the handsomest monuments in the world. Its broad front steps have become a kind of national stage for demonstrations in favor of the equality of man.

The most terrible individual tragedy in American history had taken place in Ford's Theater. The theater was closed down from that moment. It was never again used for a performance or even a rehearsal. Mobs threatened to burn it as though the place were guilty. For a while, the government used the building for offices. But in 1893 its floors fell in, killing 22 people and injuring 65 more. After that it was left virtually empty until the present time, when it is being restored to appear exactly as it was on the dreadful night in 1865.

THE TRIUMPHANT SINGULAR

The Civil War, Carl Sandburg said, was fought over a verb. Before it, people said the United States *are*. After it, people said the United States *is*. When the United States *were,* Washington was one more capital city vying with state capitals. When the United States became a unit, Washington's paramountcy was assured.

Head of the statue by Daniel Chester French in the Lincoln Memorial.

CHAPTER FIVE
WALL STREET'S POTOMAC BRANCH

A POVERTY OF RICHES

In the forty years after the Civil War, America was transformed from a nation of moderate means into a very wealthy one. With the political power of the rural South broken, Northern business was free to organize the continent's natural riches and turn them into money. Much of the wealth spilled over into the middle classes. Some seeped down into the lower classes. But most of it was held by a very few rich men, called "robber barons," who became dangerously powerful. They often used their power ruthlessly and sometimes immorally.

The city of Washington had gained enormous prestige because it had been the center of the nation's greatest war. The glory of Lincoln had brought the city a luster that grew brighter with time. People of wealth set up second homes in the city to try to acquire prestige the way you catch cold—by contagion. People without much wealth began making pilgrimages to the capital to breathe the atmosphere Lincoln had breathed.

But as Washington's prestige grew, its real power declined. Wall Street and other commercial centers replaced it as the power center. This remained so until around the turn of the century, when at last another great President would appear—rather like the prince in the story of the sleeping princess—to restore power to Washington.

THE DUEL BETWEEN THE BRANCHES

Washington subsided into a place of second-rate power only after a political clash without equal in our history. Our three branches of government were meant to balance one another. But in the aftermath of war, Congress lashed out and sought to destroy the power of the Presidency.

Cloak worn by Martha Patterson, daughter of President Andrew Johnson and First Lady of the White House.

The leaders in this duel were strongly drawn figures. One was the seventeenth President, Andrew Johnson, who succeeded to office on Lincoln's death. He was a sturdily handsome man who was self-educated, uncommonly brave, and devoted to principle. He did lack tact. But it is doubtful if all the tact in the world could have prevented what happened.

As a Senator from Tennessee he voted against Lincoln in 1860; but alone of all Southerners in Congress he voted to stay in the Union. Lincoln, always looking for ways to unite America, chose Johnson, the Southern Democrat, to run with him for Vice President in 1864.

At Johnson's inauguration as Vice President an unfortunate thing happened. Having been ill, Johnson asked to take the oath at home. It could not be done; he had to appear in the Senate chamber. To strengthen himself, Johnson, a nondrinker, took three stiff drinks of whisky. He was reeling when he stood to speak, and made a disgraceful speech. The incident was used against him.

People still argue Johnson's merits. But they do not argue about his antagonist. Crippled, embittered Congressman Thaddeus Stevens of Pennsylvania is generally regarded as a disastrous influence on the course of our history. He was the leader of the so-called "Radical" Republicans who declared war on the Presidency.

The duel arose over a number of disputes—primarily over how to bring the Southern states back into the Union. It began while Lincoln was still alive. Lincoln argued that the South had never left the Union and should be treated generously. Stevens argued that the South had left, had been conquered, and must be treated harshly.

President Andrew Johnson

Lincoln proceeded to let Southern states back in on these terms: Any state where ten percent of the people would declare allegiance to the Union, and would agree to abolish slavery, would be allowed back in with full voting rights in Congress. The Radicals fumed that Lincoln had no power to set the terms. He answered that he had the constitutional right to pardon offenders. And as Commander in Chief he could remove troops anywhere at any time.

The angry Radicals issued a manifesto saying, "The President must understand that the authority of Congress is paramount and must be respected." Asked what he thought of the manifesto, Lincoln replied:

"It is not worth fretting about; it reminds me of an old acquaintance who, having a son of scientific turn, bought him a microscope. The boy went around experimenting with his glass on everything

Johnson pardoning Southern rebels in the White House.

that came in his way. One day at the dinner table, his father took up a piece of cheese.

" 'Don't eat that, Father,' said the boy. 'It is full of wrigglers.'

" 'My son,' replied the old gentleman, taking at the same time a huge bite, 'let 'em wriggle; I can stand it if they can.' "

When Lincoln was killed, the Radicals proceeded to flood Congress with bills that were hard on the South. Johnson vetoed them all, even some reasonable ones. The Southern states did not help him. Some began reimposing Black Codes of anti-Negro laws, which gave the Radicals something legitimate to object to.

At last the Radicals sought to impeach the President—that is, to have the House of Representatives draw up a list of crimes for which the Senate would put the President on trial. This had not happened to a President before; it has not happened since.

Six times Johnson's enemies in the House tried to draw up a bill of impeachment which a majority would agree to. Each time they failed. Once they accused Johnson of being an accomplice in the murder of Lincoln! Thaddeus Stevens wanted to accuse him of "insanity or whisky," but there is no such crime.

Finally a list of eleven "crimes" won a majority vote in the House, and Johnson was put on trial in the Senate. The trial lasted two months. Johnson stayed in the White House receiving reports. His lawyers showed the charges were unfounded. But neither law nor reason counted: Passions dominated. General Grant, who no

*The House of
Representatives
impeachment committee.
Thaddeus Stevens is shown
seated, with a cane.*

longer had a war to raise him above mediocrity, paid servants to
fish through Johnson's wastepaper basket for "evidence."

Came time to vote. Two-thirds of the Senators must vote a President guilty in order to remove him from office. A Senator who was
carried into the chamber from a sick bed cast the final vote—and
thwarted a two-thirds majority against Johnson. The Radicals had
failed.

Thaddeus Stevens died within a month. Johnson was ruined as a
national figure in politics. But the Presidency was saved as a branch
of American government. For the time being, however, the Federal
government itself was exhausted. The government was now easily
dominated by the wealthy robber barons. Washington became Wall
Street's branch office on the Potomac.

WASHINGTON IN THE AFTERMATH

The White House is flanked on Pennsylvania Avenue by two much
larger buildings. On one side is the Treasury, built where Andrew
Jackson is said to have driven his walking cane into the ground. On
the other side is a much larger granite structure, which was once the
biggest office building in the world.

That second building has been the object of much criticism and
many jokes. When it was first built, the writer Henry Adams called

it "the architectural infant asylum next to the White House." But it is a very comfortable place with its high ceilings and large windows. And its construction was an especially happy event for the city. It ended for all time Washington's old fear that Congress might move the capital to another city.

Talk of abandoning the Potomac for some inland city was heard a great deal just after the Civil War. The capital came out of the war with problems that seemed insoluble. The city's economy was threatened with collapse as traffic in army supplies ended. Washington had accumulated a huge population of ex-slaves who contributed little but needed much. And the oldest problem of the city returned: Unable to tax its main enterprise, the government, the capital could not afford services deemed essential in other cities— paved streets, sewers, street lights, and the like.

But in the decade after the war some of the problems began to solve themselves. Economic collapse never came, for the federal government had grown big and important enough to be a commercial asset by itself. The city attracted new, affluent inhabitants. The large numbers of people made rich by the war found society in New York and San Francisco hard to break into, but very easy in Washington. So in they poured, filling the hotels and building extravagant new homes. Real estate, which had lagged so long in the city's early history, now became enormously profitable.

The troubles of the new population of freed slaves were met by the federal government and by the freedmen themselves. The government started public schools, founded Howard University to provide higher education, bought farms and laid out model

A Negro's first vote, 1867.

communities for some, and let others take over abandoned army barracks as homes. The fears of whites were somewhat allayed when in 1867 Washington's Negroes voted in local elections for the first time. They voted only two Negroes onto a council of twenty men to run the town. An alderman said to the new citizens about the frightened whites, "You have wrenched from them approval."

Ten years after the end of the Civil War, all government offices were badly overcrowded. Congress decided new office space was needed. The tiny War Office next to the White House, where Lincoln had gone several times a day to read dispatches from the front, was torn down. On the site was built the massive, granite edifice that provoked so much comment.

It was begun in 1871 and required seventeen years to complete. It housed three Cabinet departments—State, War and Navy. In our

time all three have outgrown it and moved elsewhere, leaving it a mere annex where the White House staff keeps offices. But at that time the great building was a national wonder—and a boon to the city, as it provided employment and incomes. Its main service, however, was psychological. It was, in the eyes of the people, a kind of giant paperweight that would hold the federal government down on the Potomac despite strong winds of discontent. With a commitment of that size it was clear that the government was not going anywhere else.

The problems of the city's economy and of the ex-slaves had been adequately dealt with. But the old problem of poor city services remained; indeed, it had grown worse since the streets had been broken by army traffic and the Tiber Creek had become a vast, sickening, open sewer. But that problem too was about to receive attention.

The State-War-Navy Building, finished in 1888 as the largest office building in the world. This photograph, taken in a later decade, also shows Pauline Wayne, President Taft's cow.

Visitor to the Smithsonian, 1881.

THE BOSS

People in Washington have had a hard time deciding whether Alex Shepherd was a villain or a hero. He bankrupted the (rather easily bankrupted) city. He is accused (rather unfairly) of having caused Congress to suspend self-government and turn Washington into a voteless colony. He was virtually forced to leave town. Yet the city commissioners, with popular approval, later built him a monument facing Willard's Hotel. And when he paid a return visit to the city, it was turned into a gay holiday.

Alexander Shepherd

This author hereby denominates him hero. Shepherd was born poor in Washington, became a good plumber, gambled in real estate, and won a fortune. His villainies were those common in America after the Civil War, when strong men bent principles in order to get rich. His virtue was that he picked the city up out of the mud and made it a gem —though using doubtful methods. But at the time it could be done no other way. And it had to be done if the city was ever to become a decent community.

Relations between Congress and its official city were at rock bottom. Congress refused to pay for anything. Mayor Wallach (editor of the *Evening Star*) pointed out that in 1791 citizens had given the government property now worth more than 100 million dollars. But Congress had devoted a total of less than 9 million dollars to Washington. Wallach called it a breach of the original agreement with the first President.

Shepherd at this point had himself appointed to the Board of Public Works. He proceeded to take over, and was soon called "The Boss." In June, 1871, he announced a plan to spend 6 million dollars of tax moneys for digging sewers and paving streets. He set to work to do in three years what other cities normally did in twenty-five. Congress and General Grant, who succeeded Andrew Johnson as President, had such an abiding respect for the robber baron type that they asked no questions.

Shepherd cagily started the work in a dozen scattered places at once. If Congress tried to stop him, it would have to go ahead and link all the scattered works—or have a mess on its hands.

Eighty miles of streets were paved in three years. Trees were planted along the streets. Parks were sodded and planted. Sewers were laced through town. Water mains were laid throughout in accordance with L'Enfant's pattern. Best of all, that old disease-spreader, the Tiber canal, was at last covered over with solid earth. Constitution Avenue marks most of its course today.

Because of the haste, sewers begun in different places failed to meet. Some of the paving broke. Shepherd went deeply into debt using money the taxpayers did not possess—but he built a brand-new Washington.

Taxpayers began complaining. Congress investigated and found that instead of 6 million dollars he had spent 18. The city could not pay its bills. Congress blasted the effort in terms that sound like qualities for an anti-boy-scout: "negligent, careless, improvident, unjust, oppressive, and illegal."

Every charge was true. But an ugly pesthole had been made into

a handsome, modern city—something Congress should have provided money for long ago. Disease fell off sharply. First Prussia, then Britain, put an international seal of approval on the city by buying land and building permanent legations.

In the Capitol rotunda, 1876.

Congress decided that the city of Washington was irresponsible and could not govern itself. In 1874 it changed the form of city government. No longer would citizens be permitted to vote. The city would be run by three commissioners, appointed by Congress. And the annual budget would be determined by Congressional committees, leaving the citizens no say whatever in how they were governed. Washington became the last American colony where taxation without representation was practiced.

In 1878 Congress decided that, since the federal government owned half the property in the city and paid no taxes, it should provide half the money to meet the city's costs. But this sensible resolve was never honored. For a while Congress met forty percent of the costs, then thirty percent; then its contribution dwindled to ten percent and below.

Shepherd was discredited and bankrupt. He moved to Mexico,

saying he would not return until he had enough money to buy the city. A popular columnist of the time, "Carp," looked at the result ten years later and wrote of Shepherd's parting statement, "If the city would pay him what she owes him for the good he did her, he might be able to supply the rest."

THE GAY CITY OF THE NINETIES

For people whose skin was white, Washington was a pleasant place to live during the rest of the century.

When Rutherford B. Hayes became President in 1877—in a deal to reinstate the South on its own terms—the process of taking away hard-gained Negro rights began. Washington barbers put signs in windows, "Haircuts $30." Below in smaller print they said, "Liberal reductions for regular customers." Restaurants also applied the two-price system to block Negro patrons.

Congress had used Shepherd's extravagance as an excuse to abolish self-rule in 1874. But another reason was to favor District of Columbia whites who wished to put an end to all voting rather than let Negroes continue to vote. In Washington, as in the nation, small groups of rich real estate men and bankers informally ran the place.

Under President Grover Cleveland, the White House had two First Ladies. His sister Rose (whose velvet dress is shown above) was First Lady until he married Frances Folsom (whose satin dress is shown below).

Wealthy people moved into the city in numbers. The inventor George Westinghouse bought a house there. Rich men got into Congress. Seventeen Senators were estimated to have combined fortunes of 600 million dollars—an almost incredible figure for that time. One Senator, Fair of Nevada, had a monthly income of some $500,000. Senator George Hearst of California was a mining millionaire. His wife, Phoebe, founded the National Cathedral School for Girls on St. Albans Hill. Their son, William Randolph Hearst, would soon become the nation's most famous newspaper publisher.

Society became second only to government as a moneymaking business. Parties were lavish. It was common to have "color" evenings, when everything from decorations to ice cream was one color —violet or pink or green.

As a result property rose in value. In a single year real estate values rose forty million dollars. Realtors bought the area around President Cleveland's house and called it Cleveland Heights. Further out they bought up Chevy Chase farm and made it a suburb.

With more money, improvements increased. The swampy edge of the Potomac was dredged to create East Potomac Park. The Jefferson Memorial is on part of the new land. What remained of the river was deepened. The Potomac, which was once clear enough for John Quincy Adams to swim in but which had turned into a mud bank, was now made clear enough for Theodore Roosevelt to swim in.

Following the assassination of President Garfield in 1881, the police force was enlarged and improved. Public buildings of massive design arose. An outstanding example was the Library of Congress, built in the Italian Renaissance style, with its Roman fountain out front. The Washington Monument was at last finished. It reduced the Cologne Cathedral to the second tallest stone structure on earth.

Alexander Graham Bell, inventor of the telephone, helped found the National Geographic Society in Washington, which began publishing an illustrated magazine. The Washingtonian John Philip So—who added the initials of his new country to his Polish name and made it Sousa—first played his "Washington Post March."

The centennial celebration of the city in 1900 was a tremendous and gay occasion. In the parade of states before the President, the

A visit to the Smithsonian, 1899.

Rhode Island delegation excited special interest by riding by in a contraption called an automobile.

Washington was livelier than ever and full of famous people not involved in politics. The city possessed everything but what George Washington meant it to have: power. The government merely provided the official stamp for decisions reached by wealthy businessmen in other parts of the nation.

In September of 1901, President McKinley was shot by an anarchist. In a few days he died. McKinley's great friend, the rich and mighty Mark Hanna of Cleveland, was heartbroken at the loss of the President. He had a second complaint too. As he put it, "Now look, that damned cowboy is President of the United States!"

The long series of undistinguished Presidents had come to an end.

THE DAY THEY BROUGHT THE POWER BACK

The "cowboy" was Theodore Roosevelt, the youngest man ever to be President. (He was forty-two. John F. Kennedy would much later be the second youngest at forty-three.) Few people ever enjoyed life as much as this New York patrician did. Son of a wealthy

Theodore Roosevelt had more zest for life, and for the Presidency, than most occupants of the White House.

Theodore Roosevelt (center, wearing glasses) with his Rough Riders.

family of Dutch descent, he went to Harvard, then dove into the hurly-burly of politics.

In an interlude of political defeat, he went out to the Dakotas to fight men, cattle, and elements and become a legend. He returned to politics and a career in which minor success alternated with minor failure. An opening to national fame came with the Spanish American War in 1898. He recruited Westerners into a regiment called "Rough Riders," pinned twelve extra pairs of steel-rimmed eyeglasses into his uniform, and went to fight.

When he returned, he was so popular that the political bosses could not keep him from being elected Governor of New York. However, they concocted a clever plan to use against this man who refused to take orders: They drafted him to run for Vice President with McKinley. They and T. R. both thought this would mean political death. He planned to study law in Washington to be able to support his family, for a political career was now out of the question.

McKinley's death put him into the White House. Now began a love affair between the nation and Teddy. Nobody since Lincoln had been so popular.

Not since the Middle Ages had a nation been so dominated by a few enormously rich men as America was in 1901. T. R. began chipping away at their power. He withdrew vast areas of mineral wealth and forestry from their exploitation and created National Parks. He persuaded Congress to pass food acts to regulate the meat industry. He forced industrialists to negotiate with workers in work stoppages—a practice unheard of then.

Undoubtedly, the most characteristic event of this time occurred when the mightiest man in America, J. P. Morgan, joined other rich men to form The Northern Securities Corporation, the biggest combine of businesses ever created. It was illegal, but these men were used to making the law fit their wishes.

There was befuddlement and shock when they were served with subpoenas: The President was suing to break up their trust. Said Morgan to his inferior, the President of the United States, "If we have done anything wrong, send your man to see my man and they will fix it up." Roosevelt answered through his Attorney General, "I don't want to fix it up. I want to stop it." He did.

From that moment, power returned to Washington. It has been misused and on occasion unused, but it has never left Washington since.

This cartoon of the period shows T.R. as Jack the Giant Killer, confronting J. P. Morgan and other powerful financiers of the time.

CHAPTER SIX
THE FIRST WORLD CRISIS

AMERICA REJOINS THE WORLD

The year Washington was burned, 1814, was also the year the nation became wholly isolationist. Americans turned away from Europe in order to concentrate on settling and exploiting the rich continent acquired by Jefferson and added to by later Presidents. Now, a hundred years later, troubles were to draw America out of isolation and back into world affairs.

Old Europe could barely recognize the returning giant. America had been a country of 4 million people when it left the British Empire. In 1900 it numbered 75 million—more than any of the European great powers save Russia. Around the turn of the century it passed all others and became the richest country on earth. In a short ten years, American farmers added to cultivation an area equal to the combined sizes of Britain and France. America's mills turned out four times as much steel in a year as those of Britain, formerly the leading producer.

But America's great strength was scattered and often wasted. Now, under the challenge of its first world crisis, a great President would harness the giant's energy. The war would be won. But the peace would be lost, for America's heart and mind had not grown as fast as its muscle and wealth.

BEAUTIFICATION RAMPANT

As the nation's wealth rose swiftly around the turn of the century, Washington received a goodly portion of the cream, in the form of stately buildings and handsome parks. Sensible Washingtonians would have also liked a steady diet of steak and potatoes, in the form of a regular flow of federal tax moneys to replace slums and improve normal city services outside the official areas of town. But the singular unfairness continued: Washington's chief enterprise, the federal government, refused to pay an appreciable portion of the costs of the city it occupied. However, at least the cream was well used. Washington entered a golden age of beautification.

The spur to action was the Chicago World's Fair. On the lakefront there a dazzling "White City" was constructed. If Chicago could improve itself, other American cities felt they could too. Washington was best able to do so, for, thanks to L'Enfant's stubbornness about his design, the federal city alone had a plan and a skeleton ready for improvement.

Congress appointed a committee on beautification. One member was the builder of Chicago's White City. The committee's recommendations in 1902 added up to one policy: Complete L'Enfant's plan.

Up to this time the Mall—the city's main park stretching from the Capitol down to the Washington Monument—was ugly with railroad tracks and switching yards. The railroads were persuaded to move, and the handsome vista to be seen today was created. With government help, the dozens of rail lines were stopped north of the Capitol, and the handsome Union Station, with its great semicircular open space in front, was built there.

Union Station

*Interior of the
Pan American Union,
built on the site of
Davey Burnes's farm.*

*Brocaded velvet dress
of the first wife
of Woodrow Wilson.*

New buildings, stately if not always beautiful, sprang up everywhere. Before, members of Congress had had to rent offices in private buildings in midtown. Now, on either side of the Capitol, official buildings were constructed for them. Eventually there would be two of these buildings for Senators and three for Representatives.

Of the many engaging nongovernment buildings that appeared, the most outstanding was the Pan American Union, with its exotic courtyard and its bouquet of many-colored marbles. It was built on the place where farmer Davey Burnes once insulted the Father of his Country. It remains an attraction today.

But while the official city was decorated with marble and was carpeted with lovely green parks, the slums expanded and congested. Theodore Roosevelt set up a commission to try to persuade Congress to vote money to replace slums. Mrs. Woodrow Wilson, shocked at what she saw on a tour of the slums, begged for action. But Congress was deaf.

Congress was now dominated by Southerners still bitter over the Civil War. The powerful chairmanships of Congressional committees go to those members with seniority—that is, those who have been in Congress the longest. Since the South had become a one-party region, and since its members thus had fewer electoral challenges, they stayed in Congress longer and accumulated seniority and power.

At this same time, from 1900 to 1910, Washington became the city with the largest Negro population in the world. Congress, dominated by embittered Southerners, would take no action to help them and the city.

THE PROF

American politics in the early part of the present century followed a rhythm. Conservative Presidents alternated with action-seeking progressive Presidents. Thus, the conservative McKinley was followed by Theodore Roosevelt, the man of action. The latter was followed by huge William Howard Taft, another conservative. In the next election year, 1912, Taft and Roosevelt, both Republicans, had a fight and split their party's vote; a Democrat won the Presidency. He turned out to be the most progressive President yet.

Thomas Woodrow Wilson has been listed by American historians in *The New York Times* as one of the four greatest of our thirty-six Presidents. There is no reason to dispute the judgment.

He had a mighty character, a brilliant intellect, and a driving ambition. These were encased in a defective body. He could not digest food and had to operate a stomach pump on himself. In a job famous for permitting little time for sleep, he needed nine hours' sleep a night.

He appeared austere and cold. In fact, he was warm and tender. He needed, and gave, an unusual amount of affection. The stonily poised public man would, in the circle of his family, become a chatterbox who mimicked others and made up improper limericks.

He was the first Southerner to be President since Andrew Johnson. He was the only college professor ever to be President. Students at Princeton had repeatedly voted him their favorite lecturer. He had written incisive studies of government. But his scholarly knowledge was his triumph and his tragedy. For, knowing much, he consulted others too little. The fate of the world was to hang upon this man tapping out policy statements on his little green typewriter in the White House.

Since Jefferson, Presidents had given up going in person to Capitol Hill to read their messages. Wilson resumed the practice of going himself. As he was a great speaker, the effect was electric. He not only spoke, he also stayed nearby and actually guided legislation to passage.

The result was the most productive period of legislation up until this time. The Federal Reserve Act was passed, bringing order and some fairness into the chaotic field of money and banking. The first income tax under the Sixteenth Amendment was a landmark of social progress. Tariffs that kept consumer prices high were cut for the first time. The national pursuit of well-being became a much fairer and more sensible activity.

Ex-President Roosevelt and President Taft, though both Republicans, were political opponents in 1912.

But now the world that America had disregarded for a century clamored for attention. The great empires of Europe had fallen into a pattern of conflict. An incident sent them to war against each other in 1914. Europe was used to wars. But technology had now advanced to where destruction could be immense. For four years, millions of men were chewed up in bloody offensives to gain or lose a few miles of trenches.

Wilson feared and hated this war. While his wife lay dying in the White House, one of his hands held hers, and his other hand pecked out on his typewriter offers to both sides to mediate and stop the war. He made the offers repeatedly.

The ocean-going Allies in Europe sought and bought war supplies in America. Their German opponents perfected the U-boat (for *Unterseeboot,* or undersea boat) and began sinking ships to try to strangle England. For a while American protests at the sinkings were heeded. But when the war intensified, the Germans began to sink without warning any ship, American or other, found in war-zone waters.

Americans began to fear that militaristic Germany might win, and that her next goal might be their own continent. The Germans secretly offered Mexico possession of Texas, New Mexico, and Arizona if Mexico would help Germany win.

As incidents and fears multiplied, Wilson felt he had to intervene. Yet he feared the prospect. He told his Secretary of the Navy, "If war comes we shall have to get the cooperation of big businessmen, and as a result they will dominate the nation for twenty years." That prophecy proved true.

He called Congress into joint session to hear a Presidential message. The sleepless night before, he called in a friendly editor just to talk. "Once lead this people to war," he said, "and they'll forget there ever was such a thing as tolerance. To fight you must be brutal and ruthless, and the spirit of ruthlessness and brutality will enter into the very fiber of life." That proved true also.

The next evening, in a blinding rainstorm, Wilson rode up to Capitol Hill. The date was April 2, 1917. The most famous passage in the speech he made to Congress was, "The world must be made safe for democracy." It became popular to scoff at that. But it is probable that had Wilson not acted, democracy might not exist in the world today.

Telling of Germany's challenges, he said, "We will not choose the path of submission." He was asking for a declaration of war. Most Senators stood and cheered.

The Senate debate afterward was long and bitter. The great Senator LaFollette of Wisconsin spoke for four hours against declaring war. The respected Senator George Norris of Nebraska opposed it too. But of 96 Senators only 7 voted against it, so war was declared.

The isolationist nation made its first frightened steps into a world that had become a raging furnace. Like a frightened person, it tended to boast and threaten. Woodrow Wilson was miserable.

THE ELEMENT OF TIME

Germany had decided to press her attacks on United States shipping, knowing it would bring America into the war. But the Germans assumed that they could strangle England and defeat the other Allies before the soft American giant could marshal strength and move into the battlefields.

This seemed a safe assumption. The Allies were hanging on by their fingernails. Britain had only enough food left for six weeks.

President Wilson asking Congress to declare war against Germany. Below: Newspaper headline, April 2, 1917.

A 1918 cartoon: France, beaten to her knees, looking hopefully to America.

The United States was so unprepared for war that recruits of 1917 had to drill with wooden howitzers.

France had been beaten in the trenches, and her troops had mutinied. Russia had undergone a revolution and would soon quit the war.

The United States had scraps of regular and National Guard troops that totaled 300,000 men. But they were without training and useful modern equipment. Not a single complete division existed.

The President made his call for action. As Winston Churchill put it in his memoirs of the First World War, "from the Atlantic to the Pacific the call was answered. . . . with a roar of slowly gathered, pent-up wrath which overpowered in its din every discordant yell, the American nation sprang to arms."

The Civil War had aroused more intense feeling. But this war was Washington's most complicated experience. The nation was now four times as big as Lincoln's nation had been. Its industry and resources, now to be mobilized, were a hundred times bigger. The President shut the usually open White House gates. He turned off the White House lights except in rooms actually in use. And he went to work.

From fragments he pieced together a single division of troops and had it in Europe within two months to encourage the weary Allies and discourage the Germans. By the end of 1917, there were 200,000 American troops in battle. In 1918 there were 2,000,000 in France with an equal number in camps in the States awaiting ships.

Wilson summoned the best talent he could find to Washington—men like Bernard Baruch, the financier, to mobilize industry; Felix Frankfurter, the law professor, to deal with labor; and Herbert Hoover, a successful young businessman, to mobilize food for Europe.

Until then, the biggest project ever undertaken by the federal government had been the digging of the Panama Canal. It took ten years. Now Wilson ordered thirty-two giant training camps constructed and equipped, a task costing nearly as much as the canal. It was completed in months.

When the railroads said they were unable to move troops and supplies fast enough, Wilson did an unheard-of thing. He took the railroads away from private management and ran them himself. They moved everything on time.

War sucked new thousands into Washington. The total population jumped in months from 350,000 to 526,000, not counting a large number of transients. The City Beautiful began to decay under the pressure. The lovely Mall, only recently cleared of railroad tracks, was filled with endless rows of temporary offices. The plaza in front of Union Station was filled with dormitories for the new government workers to live in.

The burden on city sanitation facilities reached a breaking point. For example, the city's facilities could deliver 65 million gallons of water a day. By 1918 they were breaking down under a load of 75 million gallons a day. Congress refused funds to meet this and other problems on grounds that they constituted "socialism."

So, disaster struck. In September, 1918, an influenza epidemic broke out; 35,000 people were bedridden and a tenth of them died. Hospital space and other facilities were insufficient. Bodies piled up unburied. The President called in marines from nearby Quantico to bury bodies; their camp became a hospital.

Slowly, the American effort at home and abroad turned the tide of war. Said Winston Churchill, "Of all the grand miscalculations of the German High Command, none is more remarkable than their inability to comprehend the meaning of war with the American Union."

Late in 1918 the Germans, getting hungrier and wearier, confronted with increasing numbers of fresher, better fed Americans, asked for truce terms. The request was directed not to the Allies, but to one man: the President of the United States.

World War I recruiting poster.

The American Presidency is unique among political offices. It is wholly democratic. Yet it is also infinitely elastic: A President can assume nearly dictatorial powers in time of crisis. In the First World War, Wilson exercised much more arbitrary power than the autocratic Kaiser of Germany dared use.

No other man ever used the Presidency the way Wilson did— as though it were a personal possession. As war progressed, Wilson saw his cabinet less and less and members of Congress rarely. Here was a man used to addressing classrooms and getting information from books, neither of which can talk back.

On January 8, 1918, without real advice, he issued his war settlement aims, called the Fourteen Points. The Allies seemed shocked at some points directed against colonial empires and against secret deals. But all accepted what Wilson considered his main point—Number Fourteen, which called for an organization

With the North Portico of the White House in the background, Woodrow Wilson prepares to review a parade, May, 1918.

of nations to prevent another war like this one.

When the crumbling Germans asked for terms on the basis of the Fourteen Points, Wilson settled with them virtually alone. On November 11, 1918, he scribbled with a pencil on plain paper, "My Fellow Countrymen: The armistice was signed this morning." That was how the nation heard that the war had ended.

Against the advice of many, Wilson went to Europe to negotiate peace. Europe had never—and still has never—seen anything like the reception people gave him. Crowds were so dense in Paris and London and Rome that the "savior of the world," as he was called, could hardly move. But in negotiations behind closed doors, his Fourteen Points were whittled away by irritated leaders of weary peoples. When Wilson returned to Washington, pleased to have at least retained Point Fourteen, he was much paler and thinner and his hair whiter.

Now came another terrible clash between the two ends of Pennsylvania Avenue. Voters easily grow tired of uprightness, and many were tired of Wilson. The Senate, which has to ratify foreign treaties by a two-thirds vote, was angry at not being consulted. The off-year elections put opponents of Wilson in control of both houses.

Wilson was a much greater man than Andrew Johnson. And his Congressional opponent was much more attractive than Thad-

Near the Place de la Concorde, Parisians enthusiastically welcome President Wilson.

deus Stevens. He was Henry Cabot Lodge, a graceful, handsomely bearded Boston aristocrat, chairman of the Senate Foreign Relations Committee.

Lodge disliked Wilson. He expressed the growing American disenchantment with the European Allies. He opposed America's joining the League of Nations, saying, "We would not have our politics distracted and embittered by the dissensions of other lands. We would not have our country's vigor exhausted or her moral force abated, by everlasting meddling and muddling in every quarrel, great and small, which afflicts the world."

Lodge revealed that he possessed a resolution, opposing Wilson's peace treaty and its League of Nations, signed by thirty-seven Senators—enough to prevent the two-thirds vote needed for passage.

The President was convinced that the public was with him, or would be, once it had heard his arguments. Some historians think he was right in that belief. He decided to make a speaking tour of the nation.

A cartoonist's comment, 1919.

His physician warned him against the tour. Hot trains, irregular hours, and large crowds would be too much of a strain. Also, opposing Senators had decided to send what they called a "truth squad" to speak in the same towns and harass him. Wilson answered his doctor, "I do not want to do anything foolhardy, but the League of Nations is now in its crisis, and if it fails I hate to think what will happen to the world. You must remember that I, as Commander in Chief, was responsible for sending our soldiers to Europe. In the critical test in the trenches they did not turn back—and I cannot turn back now."

Wilson went. He made forty major speeches, and many more shorter ones to smaller crowds. At that time Presidents did not have ghost writers to help them with speeches; each of Wilson's was different, composed by him, and was in a prose that few are capable of today. This was a time, too, when there were no public address systems to amplify the voice—a man had to speak loudly to be heard.

Wilson collapsed under the strain and was carried home to the White House, paralyzed by a stroke.

Our Presidential mansion had seen tragedies, but this was its worst. In the darkened mansion, its gates now chained shut, the great man lay still with only his second wife and his doctor present. He saw no one, counseled with no one. For eighteen months it seemed that America had no President. Government jobs were

vacated and left without appointments. Letters from Wilson's advisers were unanswered—indeed, some were not even opened until many years later, in 1952.

On March 19, 1920, the Senate voted on the treaty and the League of Nations. To pass it, 64 votes were needed. It received but 49. The world's strongest nation failed to join the organization its own leader had founded. The event was one of the greatest calamities in all human history. On hearing the news the President said, "If I were not a Christian I think I would go mad."

When his term had ended, the broken President moved to a house at 2340 S Street near Rock Creek Park, then the edge of the city. He lay in a replica of Abraham Lincoln's bed. (The original is in the White House.) The S Street house is today a national monument.

Crowds often gathered outside the silent house and stared at its windows. On occasion people knelt and prayed there. Once Wilson's favorite comedian, Will Rogers, came and left a message: "I am not asking to see him. Just tell him I love him."

On February 3, 1924, Wilson died. He was buried in the crypt of the Cathedral of Saint Peter and Saint Paul on Mount Alban, the highest place in the District of Columbia. He is the only known victim of both World Wars—the first one, which killed him, and the second one, which he died trying to prevent.

CHAPTER SEVEN
YEARS OF BLINDNESS

THE BOTTOM OF THE BARREL

Just before noon on March 4, 1921, an open automobile drove out of the White House driveway and up Pennsylvania Avenue. In the rear seat sat two men wearing tall silk hats. One was an old man who sat motionless, like a broken doll thrown onto a chair. The other was a sturdy and handsome middle-aged man with a most engaging smile. This was the first motor-driven Inaugural Procession. Not one person in the great crowd that watched would have guessed that in a few years the old man would be attending the robust younger man's funeral.

President Wilson (far left), next to President-elect Harding.

The old man was Woodrow Wilson. The younger man was Warren Gamaliel Harding, editor of a small-town newspaper in

Ohio and an ex-Senator, now to be the twenty-ninth President. On the scale of greatness listed in *The New York Times,* historians placed him at the bottom, a little below President Grant.

There are two favorable things to be said about Harding. First, one could disapprove of him, but it was hard not to like him. He was kind, genial, and friendly even to political opponents. One of his failings was that he was too friendly to the wrong people. Second, he knew that he was not big enough for the Presidency. He was lazy, incapable, shallow, and without discipline. He had not wanted to be President. He had been pushed forward by hard-faced men who wanted to get at public funds.

The public accepted him eagerly as a relief from the compelling Woodrow Wilson, who had reformed America and had come within inches of reforming the whole world. Americans had found their little adventure in greatness on a world stage too much for them and were running away from responsibility as though it was tainted with the plague.

Now the great iron gates of the White House, chained shut so long, were thrown open for all to come strolling in. The windows, dark so long, blazed with light. In his speeches, Warren Harding had offered the nation what he called "Normalcy." American voters thought that sounded as though it was exactly what they wanted.

THE RED SCARE

The 1920s brought the most rapid changes America had ever undergone in so short a period. Some events destined to mark those years happened before the decade began, when Woodrow Wilson's strong hand was relaxed by illness.

One was the great Red Scare of 1919 and 1920. It was caused by a combination of things.

First of all, a tiny Communist Party had just seized control of the world's largest nation, Russia. Russian Communist troops were advancing, and it seemed that similar revolutions might take place in other countries in Europe. Americans began to think that a radical handful could do the same here.

Second, during the war organized labor in America had been given a respected position of power by a federal government anxious to avoid strikes and stoppages. After the war, prices began to soar, and labor began to show its new muscle by striking for higher pay. In 1919 there were more than 3,600 strikes involving

THE NEW PRUSSIANISM.

An anti-Prohibition cartoon of 1917.

Al Capone

four million workers—more than went on strike in all the next ten years together. As a result some people found it possible to believe that the workers were trying to seize the nation's economy, as had happened in Russia.

Finally, a small number of anarchists began an insane campaign to assassinate leading Americans with bombs. Postal officials intercepted a total of thirty-six bombs addressed to leading citizens.

The climax came in Washington. Wilson's last Attorney General, A. Mitchell Palmer, was upstairs in his home one night, preparing to go to bed, when he heard a thud outside, followed by a shattering explosion. He went downstairs and found that his front door and windows had been blown in. His neighbor, a young official named Franklin Delano Roosevelt, joined him. They found debris and limbs and pieces of flesh scattered over a wide area.

No one knows what happened. But the assumption was that an assassin had lit a very short fuse on a bomb, dropped it, then had stumbled and fallen when he started to run away, and had blown himself to pieces.

The Attorney General launched a campaign against radicals of all kinds. Thousands were jailed without charges. Several hundred were deported. Some private citizens became hysterical: Mobs raided suspect offices and beat up people with foreign accents. In Washington, a man who failed to stand when "The Star-Spangled Banner" was played was shot in the back by a sailor.

When it became clear that the Russian Revolution would be confined to Russia, the scare died down. Attorney General Palmer, who had begun to hope he could run for President as the "Fighting Quaker," was ridiculed for his arrests of many people who turned out to be innocent. Now he was destroyed by a new nickname, "The Quaking Fighter."

Respectable organized labor was so afraid of being considered radical that it began leaning over backward to be unaggressive. It lost much of its power; and labor timidity was a feature of the 1920s.

THE BIRTH OF THE GANGSTER

The Eighteenth Amendment to the Constitution was ratified by January, 1919, to become effective in January, 1920. Called the Prohibition Amendment, it forbade the making, selling, and transporting of alcoholic beverages. It was the climax of a long puritanical campaign to outlaw the consumption of alcohol. The amendment passed only because the nation was preoccupied with problems of war and peace.

The trouble with Prohibition was that most Americans still wanted to drink alcoholic beverages. With a very long coastline, too long to police, and with a vast area in which liquor could be made secretly, it was impossible to keep liquor out and to enforce the Prohibition Amendment and its subsequent laws.

Placing the making and selling of alcohol outside the law simply meant handing a profitable business to those who operated outside the law. Gangs now became a major force in American life, making or importing liquor, "hijacking" shipments, "rubbing out" competitors.

The violence of the new "business" reached Washington. One day a Senator from Vermont, walking down Pennsylvania Avenue, heard shooting in a side street. He looked in and was shot himself by a bootlegger protecting his trade. But nowhere was violence as great as in Chicago, where one Alphonse Capone—known as "Scarface Al"—did 60 million dollars worth of business a year in thirst-quenching, and made a personal fortune of 20 million dollars. Eventually in the thirties he was imprisoned—not for the many murders and other serious crimes he presided over, but for not paying sufficient income tax on the proceeds.

Thus, in great part because of Prohibition, gangs became big business, and disrespect for the law became another feature of the times.

THINGS IN THE TWENTIES

Never had fads and foibles changed so rapidly. Women's dresses, whose hems had been at or near the ground for centuries, shortened until they were at the knee by 1925. Women bobbed and "shingled" their hair, and they wore straight, unfitted dresses, as though trying to become little girls by looking like them.

The first bathing beauty contest in America took place in 1921 beside the Tidal Basin in the capital. Resort owners in Atlantic City thought it such a good idea that they too held a contest the same year: The first Miss America was Miss Washington, D.C. The contest has been held in Atlantic City every year since.

A new national passion for sports produced radical results even in the capital. The Washington Senators baseball team was moved to give up its normal position near the bottom of the league and won the pennant in 1924.

Mrs. Calvin Coolidge's chiffon velvet dress. In the 1920s, for the first time in centuries, women allowed their legs to be seen; many hems of the time were at the knee.

Samuel P. Langley,
Secretary of the
Smithsonian Institution.

The great technical innovations of the time came to Washington. Automobiles multiplied on L'Enfant's broad streets. The fixing of some curious rods over the White House in 1922 announced that the national craze for radio, started in 1920, had captured President Harding.

The third great technical advance of this time was the airplane. Although most inventions are international, this was strictly an American triumph. But it was the subject of a story rather shameful for Washington.

In 1903 two bicycle makers from Dayton, Ohio, made the first airplane flights, in a plane they had constructed. They were Orville and Wilbur Wright. The plane is known by the place where the flights took place—a long windy beach near the hamlet of Kitty Hawk, North Carolina.

Two years later the British approached the Wrights and showed a military interest in their invention. The brothers patriotically offered it first to the United States Government. There are in existence some letters from the War Department, which the department would like to forget, in effect turning down the offer.

But worse than that, the Smithsonian Institution sought to deprive the Wright Brothers of recognition for their achievement. A director of the institution, Dr. Samuel P. Langley, had experimented with airplanes, but all his had plopped into the Potomac without flying. After Langley's death, the Smithsonian asked the Wright Brothers for a plane they had built much later, to be exhibited with Langley's unsuccessful early model—which would give the impression that Langley had been the pioneer.

And much worse still, the Smithsonian permitted a commercial competitor of the Wrights to take the old Langley model out to a workshop, secretly change it in accordance with the Wrights' plane, then fly it to establish the claim for Langley. (Dr. Langley himself made no such claim, and all his relations with the Wrights during his lifetime were cordial and fair.) Fortunately, photographs of the Langley plane before and after existed to reveal the fraud.

Patiently and good-humoredly, Orville Wright sought through the twenties to induce the Smithsonian to put the record right. Finally, in 1928, he gave up and yielded to an earlier British request that the *Kitty Hawk* be exhibited in the Science Museum in London.

With the facts on exhibit on the two sides of the Atlantic for experts to compare, the whole world gave the Wrights credit. But the Smithsonian did not agree to correct the record it published in annual reports until 1942. The *Kitty Hawk* was not returned for installation in the Smithsonian until 1948, just after Orville Wright's death.

In 1927 Charles Lindbergh had better luck. He flew his little airplane, *The Spirit of St. Louis,* alone across the Atlantic from New York to Paris. America badly needed a hero in an unheroic time, so no one complained when the President sent a war cruiser to France to fetch back man and plane. That plane, too, is in the Smithsonian.

BOTTOMING OUT

The pursuit of pleasure and of money is evil only when they become the chief aims of life. In the twenties that nearly happened. There was a marked decline in generosity and civic spirit. Washington suffered because it needed these qualities rather more than other cities.

The official parts of town continued to progress simply because the federal government had to use them and therefore put money into them.

The great triangle of land whose long sides are Pennsylvania Avenue and the Mall was purchased by the government. There arose the great complex of neat but uninspired buildings known as the Federal Triangle. They include the Departments of Commerce, Labor, Justice, and the Post Office, and the Archives Building, where the Constitution and other documents are kept. Later a device was constructed in the Archives Building whereby the Constitution and the Declaration of Independence can, at the push of a button, be lowered into an unbreakable underground vault in the event of some peril like a bombing.

In 1921, the tomb of the Unknown Soldier of World War I was dedicated on the grounds of Robert E. Lee's Arlington plantation. There were few bridges across the Potomac, so the biggest traffic jam ever took place as cars waited in line to cross to Arlington. After four hours of waiting and gasoline fumes, members of Congress were ready to vote for a new bridge: today's beautiful, low-arched Memorial Bridge, behind the Lincoln Memorial.

A year later, the Lincoln Memorial was dedicated on artificial ground dredged out of the Potomac. The tremendous seated figure of the greatest American measures nineteen feet from its base to the top of the bowed head. In the half-light of the temple at night, it is one of the great sights of America.

But in other respects, life in Washington deteriorated in spirit.

Wilbur Wright:
a 1910 comment
in picture and verse.

THERE WAS A YOUNG FELLOW NAMED WRIGHT
WHO STUDIED THE BIRDS IN THEIR FLIGHT.
" IF THESE SPARROWS CAN FLY,
WHY IN THUNDER CAN'T I?"
QUOTH HE, AND HE PROVED HE WAS RIGHT.

HERE RESTS IN
HONORED GLORY
AN AMERICAN
SOLDIER
KNOWN BUT TO GOD

Tomb of the
Unknown Soldier

The intolerance Wilson predicted became a fact. Supported by a Supreme Court ruling in 1926, real estate dealers wrote clauses into most sale and rental contracts forbidding Negroes and Jews to live in the new areas of the expanding city. In an orgy of racial exclusivity, they began to exclude still others: Arabs, Slavs, and—as the witticism had it—"everybody except me and thee, with some doubts about thee."

Negroes suffered most. This fact is particularly bitter, for when Wilson called for volunteers to fight the war, Negroes responded gallantly. Of the 480 Washington Negroes accepted, 25 won the French Croix de Guerre. White troops who returned were given a parade in Washington. But when the "First Separate Battalion" of Negroes returned, no one thought of a parade.

Washington's two leading newspapers, now among the very finest anywhere, were then part causes of deterioration. The old *Evening Star* was bland to the point of being cowardly about reporting news. And the *Washington Post* was a shrill provoker of race troubles. Its false reports that "Men in Uniform Attack Negroes as Climax to Assaults on White Women" encouraged hoodlums to enter Negro neighborhoods every night for a week to beat up inhabitants.

Had Washingtonians but known it, there was some comfort to be had in the situation. The long decline in Negro rights since the previous century was now "bottoming out"—reaching its low point

Negro volunteers of World War I with the Croix de Guerre, awarded for bravery in action.

and preparing to rise. The organization of the Community Chest in 1928, with whites and Negroes brought together in a community effort, is often thought to have been the turning point toward equality. But at that time the upswing was not evident.

Congress not only decreased its payments to the city, but began to postpone and then cancel the "D.C. days," when it was supposed to act as a government for the District and meet Washington's problems. Perhaps the best commissioner the city ever had, Louis Brownlow, resigned at this time to become the city manager of a town in Virginia. Though the town had but one-fourteenth as many people as Washington, it offered twice the salary and none of the endless headaches.

Throughout the nation money overflowed. Pleasure was King. Harding was immensely popular. What a shock, then, when in 1923 he died suddenly in San Francisco. His body was returned to Washington by a special train. Everywhere on the way, crowds gathered and stood silent or prayed.

Had no more been known of Harding than the public knew then, he would have had a pleasant place in memory. But some Senators knew what Harding also knew at his death, and the public was soon to hear about it too.

THE LITTLE GREEN HOUSE ON K STREET

The number of the house was 1625. It was a block north of Lafayette Square, which made it three blocks from the White House. It looked like a modest Victorian home.

A number of small-caliber politicians from Harding's home state rented it, and it became known as the headquarters of the "Ohio

Gang." Despite Prohibition, liquor was to be had there by the bottle or the case. Big poker games, some with the President holding a hand, went into the night and morning. It became known that if you wanted a favor in Washington and were willing to pay for it, the place to go was the little green house at 1625 K Street.

Senators heard complaints and studied some facts. One thing hard to overlook was the change in the Secretary of the Interior, a grubby looking man named Albert B. Fall. He had been shabby and near bankruptcy when Harding appointed him. In a short while his affairs showed signs of great and sudden prosperity.

We do not have space to go into all the complex details. But the main development was this: The Navy Department owned some rich oil lands, for use in the event of war and a sudden need for fuel. Harding ordered the lands transferred from the Navy Department to Secretary Fall's Department of the Interior. Fall then began secretly leasing the lands to private oilmen. Large gifts soon showed up in his possession, and his bank accounts sharply increased. There was no way to fend off a conclusion that he had been bribed, and that public property was being pilfered.

This was the great Teapot Dome scandal, named after the physical appearance of one of the oil properties in Wyoming. But there were many lesser scandals. The director of the Veterans' Bureau was found to be enriching himself by selling government property. The Alien Property Custodian was caught selling valuable captured German patents at nice prices. And so on.

Harding knew that the facts were about to break when he went off on a trip to Alaska. On the way home he apparently contracted food poisoning. While he was recovering in a hotel in San Francisco, he developed pneumonia. Suddenly he died from a clot on the brain.

People connected with Harding began dying or disappearing. The director of the Veterans' Bureau fled to Paris and refused to come home until much later. Harding's wife and his doctor died. Five of the frequenters of 1625 K Street died or committed suicide, or—the sensational version says—were murdered by those seeking to keep other details from being known.

Such was the mood of the twenties that at first the press criticized the investigating Senators more than they criticized the pillagers. The nation subscribed to funds for a monument to Harding in his hometown, Marion, Ohio. But as the facts became known, his successors as President grew increasingly reluctant to go to Marion to dedicate the monument. Year after year such a dedication was

Song cover of Coolidge campaign.

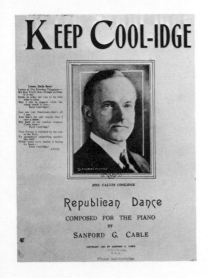

postponed—until 1931, when two Presidents faced up to it and went to Marion together.

KEEPING COOL

The nation was too prosperous to change parties in the next elections. It heeded the campaign slogan to "Keep Cool with Coolidge," the Vice President who had replaced Harding.

Calvin Coolidge is most famous for his silences. He rarely talked. At White House dinners he would at a certain time glance at his watch and go upstairs to bed without saying anything to the guests. Some of his infrequent utterances were not trying to the brain, as when he stated this definition: "When a great many people are unable to find work, unemployment results."

Never was there a period when so little was said and so few decisions made in the White House. At one time Coolidge's silence was identified with sharp Yankee wisdom. History's verdict is that he was silent because he had nothing to say.

A cartoonist's comment, 1926.

The years of dismal leaders came to an end with the election of another Republican, Herbert Clark Hoover, as President in 1928. Hoover was a man of stature. Back in 1920, Democrats had talked of drafting him to run as their candidate.

He was our most traveled President. As an engineer and businessman he traveled the five continents, and his home was in London when the First World War broke out. In an age when businessmen were highly thought of, he was a successful one. He was a first-class administrator and one of the best Secretaries of Commerce the nation has had. He was a humanitarian who, at President Wilson's request, organized the food supplies that kept Europe alive during and after the Great War.

In his inaugural address in March, 1929, he was able to point to the greatest prosperity the nation had ever enjoyed, and to promise that poverty would soon be stricken from the land for the first time in history. No President ever looked out on fairer prospects.

That was seven months before the bottom fell out and the roof fell in.

An unemployed worker selling apples within sight of the Capitol.

THE GREAT DEPRESSION

Economics is often called the Dismal Science. It is rather dull and hard to understand. Yet economic factors can cause distress and even social upheaval. The Great Depression that began in 1929 is considered by many to be—next to the Civil War—the worst experience America has ever undergone, causing more anxiety than either world war.

In 1929, not very much was understood about economics. This failure to understand was one of the greatest failures in Washington's history, so the following rough and simplified explanation has a place here.

After the Civil War, America created wealth at a great rate. But the wealth was distributed unevenly. The people who used most of their money to buy the goods turned out by machines received too little income. The people who spent most of their income investing in more machines to turn out more goods received too much. As a result, America had too many machines turning out goods that not enough people were buying. So plants were shut down and men unemployed on a huge scale.

The Depression was triggered by a stock market crash. The main way people invest money is in buying shares in companies, in the form of stock sold on the stock market. Throughout the 1920s, so many people were bidding for stocks that prices rose far above any real value. In September and October, 1929, investors finally grew frightened that values would fall, so they rushed to sell out, causing stock prices to collapse. The value of stocks listed by *The New York Times* fell from 450 points to 255 points in those two months. In the first three years of the Depression, the stock of U.S. Steel, then the biggest corporation, fell from $262 per share to $22.

As plants shut down and laid off workers, the number of unemployed reached fifteen million people.

The rest of the world was also hit by the Depression. But few nations were hit as hard as the United States, and in no other country did the Depression last as long. As America was by far the richest country, the contradictions of poverty-amid-plenty seemed worse here. Farmers burned crops because they could not make enough to live on by selling them, while other Americans suffered for lack of food.

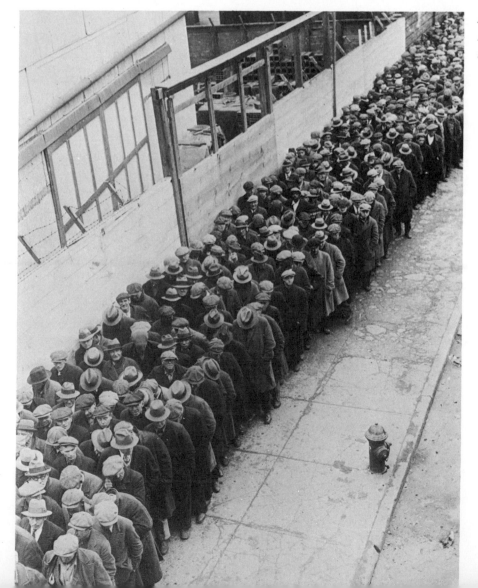

Penniless victims of the Depression, waiting in line to be fed.

At that time one of the usual treatments recommended for economic recession was to cut all costs by laying off as many workers as possible, and to reduce government spending to rock bottom. This was what President Hoover sought to do, and what his more famous successor in the White House promised to do. The treatment was rather like trying to cure a pneumonia patient by standing him in the rain.

Today we know that we must do the opposite. When depression threatens, the government must increase spending to put more money into circulation; as people spend more and factories need more workers, the economy will revive. Both Democratic and Republican administrations in Washington have followed this course in recent years.

But in the early years of the Depression, like a mighty giant waylaid by sprites it can neither see nor feel, the nation wallowed in frustration it could not overcome or even understand.

CITY OF DESPAIR

People looked to Washington, and Washington looked away. The city could not even take care of itself. Despite the continuation of much federal building, unemployment in the capital began to rise. One worker in four in the city lost his job. In 1933 Congress did not even vote the city a budget.

In 1931 some "Hunger Marchers" came to town. But nothing happened, so they left.

In May, 1932, a more serious demonstration began. Veterans of World War I were being paid a bonus for their service. But the bonus was coming in very slow installments—the major portion would not be due for thirteen more years. The veterans asked Congress to pay them the whole bonus now, in 1932, when they needed it most. To back up their request they marched on Washington. The marchers began in Oregon, and gathered numbers as they crossed the nation, riding the train rails, in old jalopies, or on foot. At one time or another, an estimated 80,000 men joined the march on the federal city. Some wives and children trailed after them.

The chief of the Washington police force, General Pelham Glassford, is one of the city's unsung heroes. As the distraught veterans poured in, he cleared unused government buildings for them to sleep in; then he helped them set up shantytowns beyond the Eastern Branch in what was called the Anacostia Flats. He contributed a good deal of his own income to help feed them.

The House of Representatives passed the Bonus Bill calling for immediate payment. The night the Senate debated the bill, the bonus marchers gathered on the Capitol lawn until sprinklers were turned on to chase them off the grounds. When the news came that the Senate had killed the bill, the veterans were angry, but they retreated with discipline, singing "America" as they returned to their dreary quarters.

Many went home. But others stayed on, using as their slogan, "Stay till the bonus is granted—no radical talk, no panhandling, no booze." When there were only 10,000 left, President Hoover

Bonus marchers on the Capitol lawn.

General Douglas MacArthur (right) and Major Dwight Eisenhower (partly hidden at left) conferring about the bonus marchers.

ordered Chief of Police Glassford to throw them out of town. Glassford argued that it was a national problem, not just a Washington, D.C., problem. But when the President insisted, Glassford moved on the marchers, and in a clash two men were killed.

The President then ordered the U.S. Army to throw the marchers out. Troops assembled on the Ellipse green just south of the White House. In command was a dapper general named Douglas MacArthur. In charge of his tanks was a bright-faced young major named Dwight Eisenhower.

The troops put on gas masks, then moved down Pennsylvania

Avenue forcing the men out of the unused federal buildings. After that, troops crossed the river and cleared the men out of their shantytowns. The burning shacks created a lurid background to the Capitol.

MacArthur said there would have been a revolution, had the troops not moved in. The Attorney General said that the marchers brought "the largest aggregation of criminals that had ever been assembled in this city at one time." Perspective and time were to indicate that neither statement was true. The marchers were well behaved. And aside from the baseball park, they were the only racially integrated feature of the city.

The White House gates were shut again. The man inside, once affable, grew bitter. His name had been made into a verb, to "hooverize," which meant to get things done efficiently. Now his name was applied to all the shantytowns of the unemployed in America; they were called "Hoovervilles."

In the long evening of his life, Hoover was to recover much of his reputation. The country eventually recognized that he was a victim of the conventional wisdom of his time, which happened to be dead wrong. What was needed then was not for Washington to lead less, but for Washington to lead much, much more.

Hooverville, 1932.

CHAPTER EIGHT
THAT MAN IN THE WHITE HOUSE

THE HAPPY WARRIOR

We have mentioned earlier the list of American Presidents tabulated by historians and published by *The New York Times*. In the topmost group on the list, the great Chief Executives, five names appear. Numbers one and two are Lincoln and Washington. Numbers four and five are Wilson and Jefferson. We now come to the figure whom the historians have rated as our third greatest President. He is of special importance to this book, for during his Presidency Washington for the first time became a big city and the paramount world capital.

Franklin Delano Roosevelt brought to politics a magic name and an uncommonly winning charm. Supreme Court Justice Oliver Wendell Holmes was to sum him up later as "a second-class intellect—but a first-class temperament." Holmes was given to frank appraisals. It was he who as a young major had told Lincoln at Fort Stevens, "Get down, you fool!"

Franklin was a much-removed cousin of Theodore Roosevelt, and he married Theodore's niece, Eleanor—a lanky, shy, toothy girl who, like Lincoln, made homeliness quite beautiful. On the strength of his name and charm, he had been the Democratic Vice-Presidential candidate in 1920—the year of the Republican landslide for Harding. The next year, Roosevelt was struck down by infantile paralysis, and many thought that his political career was over. He spent years in study and thought, and trying to teach his muscles to move.

In 1924, New York Governor Alfred E. Smith drew Roosevelt out of retirement by persuading him to make the speech nominating Smith for President. Roosevelt's speech called Smith "the happy warrior." The term might better have been applied to the gay,

Franklin D. Roosevelt (right) was the Democratic candidate for Vice President in the year when James M. Cox (left) lost to Harding.

combative Roosevelt himself.

Against his will he was drafted to run for Governor of New York, and he won. When the Depression hit the nation, this interesting figure—with his handsome, massive head and strong bull-like torso, mounted on almost lifeless legs—rose to the top of American politics as though propelled by natural forces. The results of the 1932 elections were sweeping. Roosevelt won the Presidency easily. His party carried the House of Representatives 313 seats to 117, and the Senate 59 to 37.

The few months on either side of January, 1933, were among the most anxious in American history. Fifteen million people were without work. Banks, unable to pay depositors, were falling like cardhouses in a wind. The bottom was reached on March 4, 1933, the day Franklin Roosevelt made his laborious way to the lectern outside the Capitol to take the Presidential oath. The weather was dark and drizzling. It was, a newspaper said, the "blackest inauguration since Lincoln's."

Roosevelt's clear, ringing voice sounded hope and determination. "We have nothing to fear but fear itself," he said. He would ask Congress to give him "broad executive power to wage a war against the emergency, as great as the power that would be given to me if we were in fact invaded by a foreign foe." He ended, "The people . . . have made me the present instrument of their wishes. In the spirit of the gift, I take it." When he said these words, the drizzle had stopped and the clouds had parted, and the sun came streaming through.

Within twenty-four hours, he had assumed the same financial powers Wilson used in World War I. He summoned Congress back into special session. There began the "Hundred Days" of action.

THE NEW DEAL

Throughout the campaign and early in his first term, Roosevelt had shared the old belief that the situation would somehow improve if government spending was cut. This brief period caused greater distress. He soon abandoned the idea for its opposite—a program of action called the New Deal.

In the short special session, he asked Congress to pass fifteen major acts. Senator Bertrand Snell, the Republican leader, expressed the mood of Congress: "The house is burning down and the President of the United States says this is the way to put out the fire." Congress passed everything.

Prohibition was modified and later repealed.

A large amount of money was distributed to people through public works, useful and not so useful. Harry Hopkins, the President's favorite aide, began projects before he had an office. He had distributed five million dollars in the first two hours. By the next winter, the programs were providing jobs for four million people.

The AAA (Agricultural Adjustment Act) paid farmers to plow under crops, slaughter livestock to keep it off the market, and limit new planting. As a result, the program got money into the empty pockets of the farmers.

The CCC (Civilian Conservation Corps) gave jobs to 300,000 youths. By the time the project ended, it had employed ten times that number. The young people were taken off the streets and into the country to work on conservation projects and earn money.

The TVA (Tennessee Valley Authority) began to build a chain of dams along the winding Tennessee Valley, supplying electric power cheaply where it had not existed before, and rescuing land from erosion.

The NIRA (National Industrial Recovery Act) negotiated "codes" of wages and prices for private firms to get money flowing in the economy. The SEC (Securities Exchange Commission), established in 1934, limited speculation on the stock market. Social Security in 1935 began to provide payments to the unemployed and the elderly.

Much else was done. Briefly, the main effect was to redistribute incomes downward to the people who needed help most, and whose purchases would do most to revive business.

THE REVIVING CITY

The President's brief adventure in cost-cutting, coming on top of Hoover's cuts, had hurt Washington painfully. Roosevelt ordered a fifteen per cent cut in all federal salaries. Every employee who had a spouse employed in government was dismissed. Over 17,000 people lost their government pensions. And 28,000 houses in the city were put up for sale because the owners could not pay their taxes.

But when these economy moves were abandoned, things improved promptly. In the first year of the New Deal, federal jobs in the city increased from 63,000 to 93,000.

As in previous national crises, people came to Washington in droves—businessmen to negotiate price "codes," union men to set up offices and argue about wages, reporters to gather and sell the city's chief commodity, news. It was estimated that 40,000 people were entering the city every day through Union Station.

The quality of the new citizenry was as important as its quantity. At the bottom of the scale were poor Negroes from the South, in great numbers. At the top scholars came in, fleeing the new scourge of Nazism in Europe. (One of them, transferring from Goettingen in Germany to George Washington University, was Edward Teller, in time to be known as "the father of the H-Bomb.")

The government of the city itself entered a low period. The President and his increasing army of zealous helpers were busy running a nation, and he proceeded to make some of the worst appointments ever to the three commission offices that govern the city.

But public works, and some private ones, made the city handsomer. Facing the Federal Triangle, the beautiful National Gallery of Art—a gift of former Secretary of the Treasury Andrew Mellon —began to rise on the Mall in 1937.

The chief controversy of the time was over the design and location of the large, low-domed monument to Thomas Jefferson. When workers came to remove a row of cherry trees on the Tidal Basin in order to dig foundations for it, they found women protesters had chained themselves to the trees. The women believed that the monument would spoil the view from the White House.

When completed, the monument actually improved the view. If there is a moral to the episode, it may be that good monuments take time to mature into reality. Such quickly constructed figures as the Robert A. Taft Memorial on the Capitol grounds, and the Sam Rayburn Monument in the newest House Office Building, are awkward and ordinary beyond expression. But Lincoln's Memorial, erected half a century after his death, and Jefferson's, built a century after his death, are magnificent. There has been a big dispute about a monument to F.D.R. Possibly, the time taken to decide on it will make the eventual monument worthy of the man.

NEW OLD GEORGE TOWN

An unplanned achievement of the New Deal was the revival of Georgetown, where L'Enfant drafted his plan for the national capital.

A century ago, Georgetown had entertained hopes of becoming a great commercial center. But the land nearby was exhausted from too many tobacco crops, and the C & O Canal failed to beat the railroad and the Erie Canal to the West. Furthermore, the Potomac silted up with mud at a time when steamships required even deeper harbors than sailing ships had needed.

People of means drifted away. Poor Negro immigrants from the South drifted in to occupy cheap, run-down old houses. In 1895, the place was formally absorbed by the constantly expanding city of Washington, and the name of Georgetown was officially abolished.

Now, the young scholars and lawyers of the New Deal worked six days a week, then took walks on the seventh day. They discovered the handsome village, a little down-at-the-heels but still very interesting, right in the city. One by one they began buying up the houses cheaply and renovating them.

Gas light in Georgetown

This began about 1934. By 1950, residents persuaded Congress to set up a Fine Arts Commission to regulate all new building and make it conform to what was already there. By 1954, Georgetown was a luxury neighborhood and one of the most charming urban spots anywhere. It is a delight to the eye to walk its shaded sidewalks past its handsome houses. And it is a delight to the memory to identify homes with some of the famous people who have lived in them. Many residents recall the brick house on N Street from which each morning an inordinately young-looking Senator used to leap down the steps, and after flagging a cab wave goodbye to the pretty young woman and the little girl named Caroline in the doorway.

The only official elected by the American people as a whole is the President. (They may not choose the Vice President; the President has already chosen him.) As a result, there is a special bond between the people and the President. They want to know him and all about him. Few Presidents ever gained such a grip on their interest— hostile and friendly alike—as the second Roosevelt.

He made sure they found out all about him.

He invented the modern press conference. He invited reporters in, and they fired questions freely, and he fired back the answers "from horseback." The press conferences became the best show in Washington. Editors who used editorial columns to criticize the President were perplexed to find their attacks cancelled out because they had to devote half their front pages to favorable news about him—news created by Roosevelt in his press conferences.

He studied the gadget Harding had installed—the radio—and began using it. He started a series of "fireside chats" that carried his ringing voice into every American home. The fireside chat became a feared weapon among politicians. The mere threat to take up a certain topic in a chat was known to change votes in Congress.

The American people discovered that the aristocrat they had

Georgetown houses

elected had an earthy touch that few coal miners could equal. His clothing was ever rumpled and baggy. He ate anything put before him except spinach (the word "Spinach!" was one of his strongest oaths when he was vexed), which means that his palate was not very discriminating. If Jefferson raised White House food to a peak of quality, Roosevelt carried it to the bottom. He allowed his wife but $2,000 a month to run a mansion that could use four or five times that sum. A small boy, invited to the White House for lunch along with his father, came out and told reporters, "The food stank!"

The famous playwright Robert Sherwood once wanted twenty minutes with the President, but the President's secretary said he could stay only five minutes. So Sherwood went out and bought a huge bag of peanuts. "What have you got there?" Roosevelt asked when Sherwood appeared. The writer revealed his treasure—and spent forty minutes with the President talking and eating peanuts.

Roosevelt had a gay sense of humor. Especially, he loved needling his critics. When he spoke to a convention of the Daughters of the American Revolution, who are super-conscious of their American ancestry, he addressed them as "Fellow Immigrants!" That may be the reason why—when the Republicans finally returned to office—the D.A.R. asked that the nation's gold reserves buried in Fort Knox be counted to make sure they were all there!

This aristocratic reformer aroused a hatred among the well-to-do that is hard to explain. Some refused to use his name and simply referred to him as "that man in the White House." One dowager

Left: FDR preparing for a "fireside chat." Right: "Press Conference at the White House," a cartoon by Gluyas Williams.

never wrote his name except with a small r.

Throughout most of our history, Americans have had a sharp prejudice against strong central government—perhaps because our nation was born in a bitter fight against a distant government in England. Those to whom the words "the Government" and "Washington" were evil words, and those who developed a powerful dislike for "That Man," decided in 1936 that they had had enough. They were resolved to throw him out in the 1936 elections. One of the leading magazines of the time was *The Literary Digest*. It polled the public and prophesied that Roosevelt would be defeated when he ran for a second term.

Democrats fretted. Republicans were expectant. Only the Postmaster General, James A. Farley, who was also Roosevelt's campaign manager, predicted that his boss would win in a landslide. When the votes were counted, Farley was right. Only Vermont and New Hampshire went to the opponent. Roosevelt carried 46 of the 48 states. *The Literary Digest* went out of business.

FDR in a jaunty mood.

On Election Day, 1936, Roosevelt seemed mightier than any President had ever been in time of peace. But his victory was almost too complete. It was one of those summits from which the only further movement is downward.

NINE OLD MEN

Earlier in this book we observed that the Supreme Court was the poor sister of the three branches of the federal government. It had no home of its own to match the Capitol and the White House. It met for more than a century and a third in box-cluttered basements, taverns, and disused rooms in the Capitol where, without a robing room, the Justices had to put on their cloaks behind an improvised screen.

At last in 1935 the Supreme Court acquired a splendid home of its own to match the great buildings of the other two branches. On the spot where the brick Capitol had been built after the burning of the city in 1814, a very large and dazzling pink-white marble temple was constructed for the sole use of the Court.

From its shining new palace, facing the Capitol, the Supreme Court did what Congress feared to do. It began opposing and destroying the New Deal. It first ruled that the NIRA was unconstitutional. In a series of further rulings, it killed the AAA and crippled other New Deal acts. Roosevelt was in a frustrated fury at the actions of the "nine old men" of the Court.

At Roosevelt's second inauguration in 1937, the central tableau of the swearing-in on the Capitol steps featured two of the finest chins in the nation jutting defiantly at one another—the fine, bearded one of the Chief Justice, Charles Evans Hughes, and the smooth, aggressive one of the President.

Supreme Court Building

The Chief Justice's voice rose when he came to that part of the President's oath which stated the "promise to support the Constitution." Roosevelt said later that he wanted to answer by inserting the words, "Yes, but the Constitution as I understand it, flexible enough to meet any problems."

One day, a month after that inauguration, the nine Justices were seated on their high dais hearing a case when the curtains behind them parted. A messenger came through and placed a piece of paper before each Justice. Some blanched. All were visibly shaken.

The sheets of paper each contained a statement the President had made that same morning. He had called Congressional leaders to the White House and told them he was asking Congress for authority to appoint an additional Justice for each one now over the age of seventy who had served on the high bench at least ten years. Altogether, he wanted authority to add six new judges, more than enough to outvote the conservative majority who were killing his legislation.

"The big issue," Roosevelt told reporters that same morning, "is this: Does the decision [of the Court to kill legislation] mean that the United States has no control over any economic problem?"

In fact, Roosevelt's plan was not radical when compared to past practice. Presidents have regularly warred against the Court and used stronger weapons than FDR's. As we saw earlier, Jefferson persuaded Congress to impeach a Justice in an attempt to cow the whole court. Jackson had once simply refused to carry out its ruling. Roosevelt merely sought to change the number of Justices—a step that had been taken six times before in our history.

But mistrust of the power Roosevelt had accumulated had grown to the point where resistance was about to form against him. The Court fight provided an opportunity. The members of Congress whom he had called to the White House to hear his plan listened in silence. They returned in silence to the Hill. Finally one of them, Hatton Sumners of Texas, Chairman of the House Judiciary Committee, said, "Boys, this is where I cash in." That statement marked the end of Congress's obedience to FDR. The Senate Judiciary Committee rejected his Court plan by a vote of 10 to 8.

The President sought to rescue his prestige by offering a compromise plan to Congress. One day, he summoned his Vice President, John Garner of Texas, who knew much more about Congress than Roosevelt did. This exchange took place:

Above: The Blue Eagle was the symbol of the NRA (which administered Roosevelt's NIRA). Below: Cartoonist's comment when the Supreme Court declared the NIRA unconstitutional.

FDR: "How does it look, Jack?"
Garner: "How do you want it, with the bark on or off?"
FDR: "Give it to me the rough way."
Garner: "You haven't got the votes."

Roosevelt had lost his first major battle. It was a step down a slippery slope.

A GREAT CHIEF JUSTICE

Franklin Roosevelt so dominated the 1930s that it is sometimes forgotten that other giants inhabited Washington in those years.

One reason he lost his Court fight was that his opponent was Chief Justice Charles Evans Hughes. A former Governor of New York, Hughes had run as the Republican candidate for President

*FDR with his
first-term Vice President,
John Nance Garner.*

in 1916 and nearly beaten Woodrow Wilson. He was a man of great integrity and monumental dignity. Men so nearly statuesque are often the butts of ridicule. Theodore Roosevelt called him "the old lady with a beard."

There is a delightful true story about him. On election night, 1916, he was leading Wilson handily. Much later in the night, a reporter knocked on his door and asked to see him. A butler answered, "The President has gone to bed." The reporter said, "Well, when he wakes up, tell him he is not President." The tide had turned to Wilson.

But Hughes was a shrewd and a great man. Some believe that he ranks with John Marshall and Earl Warren as one of our great Chief Justices.

Hughes was not a member of the conservative majority on the Court which consistently ruled out Roosevelt's laws. He understood that the Court could not simply frustrate every solution to current problems enacted by the President and Congress and clearly approved of by most people. No one can be sure, but it is suspected that he approached one of the conservative Justices for a heart-to-heart talk. The conservative, Justice Owen Roberts, suddenly switched sides on the next ruling and provided a majority in favor of Roosevelt's legislation. Hughes said to him, "Roberts, you may have saved the country."

Before long, conservative Justices began to retire. Roosevelt began naming to the Court men attuned to his program. So the New Deal actually won in the end. But the political prestige of the President had been dealt a blow which proved hard to recover from.

THE LION OF LABOR

In the 1930s, perhaps the most famous man in Washington next to the President was John Llewellyn Lewis, a labor leader of Welsh extraction with a lion's mane of hair and a Celtic gift of eloquence.

One day in 1937, Lewis sat down to lunch in Washington's Mayflower Hotel. At a nearby table sat Myron C. Taylor, head of the U.S. Steel Corporation, and Mrs. Taylor. Taylor, one of the nation's biggest businessmen, and Lewis, the nation's foremost labor organizer, were considered natural enemies. Nevertheless, Mrs. Taylor now urged her husband to invite Lewis over to join them for lunch. Taylor finally did so, and Lewis accepted. The luncheon that ensued did a great deal to change America.

John L. Lewis

Lewis had long been head of the Mine Workers Union. He had been an arch-conservative in politics and had campaigned for Coolidge and Hoover. But with the passage of New Deal laws that encouraged workers to join unions and bargain for a greater share of the national wealth, he became a supporter of FDR. "It takes every man some time to find himself in this world," Lewis said. "It took me longer than most."

He launched a membership drive that tripled the number of miners in his union. Then he began a campaign to organize workers in industries that had hitherto forbidden unions. The most important of these was the steel industry, of which Taylor's corporation was the biggest unit.

His campaign to organize the unorganized was stormy. His first opposition came from labor itself. The great national federation of unions, the A.F.L. (American Federation of Labor), was dominated by skilled craftsmen, who feared Lewis would dilute their power by bringing in millions of unskilled workers. Lewis and William Green, head of the A.F.L., had a titanic fight in which the miners' leader said of the latter, "I fear his threats as much as I believe his promises." Finally, Lewis broke with the A.F.L. and formed his own federation in Washington, the C.I.O. (Congress of Industrial Organizations).

Then came the actual struggle to unionize the reluctant industries—mainly steel, automobile, glass, and rubber. Some of the managements accumulated large arsenals of firearms, and much bloodshed followed. Said Lewis, "They are smiting me hip and thigh. . . . right merrily shall I return their blows." The workers' main tactic in their struggle to unionize industries was to hold sit-down strikes in many factories—a tactic whereby strikers could prevent strikebreakers from replacing them.

Labor-management relations became unusually bitter. The nation was therefore all the more astounded when, after weeks of secret talks—which had begun with that lunch in the Mayflower—U.S. Steel announced that Taylor had agreed voluntarily to let Lewis organize the workers of that great corporation.

Pitched battle between police and striking steelworkers in Chicago.

There were further troubles. But after that Lewis's campaign could no longer be halted. In a few years the number of workers in unions increased from 2 million to 8 million.

THE DECLINE OF THE NEW DEAL

The period of Lewis's high prominence dealt President Roosevelt two blows. First, photographs of grinning workers in possession of factories frightened some people into believing a revolution was breaking out. Propertied people began contributing more money to propaganda and election campaigns to curtail Roosevelt's power in Washington.

Second, after a while Lewis—a temperamental man—turned against the President. Secretary of Labor Frances Perkins has written that Lewis demanded to be made Vice President of the United States, and Roosevelt refused. In any case, Lewis added his considerable weight to the forces opposing the President.

Roosevelt's assault on the Supreme Court, the new fear in the hearts of businessmen, and the opposition of men like Lewis hastened the decline of the New Deal's popularity. But the chief cause of decline was that the program of action had failed to end the Depression. The American economy was a much bigger and more dynamic machine than was generally realized at that time. Roosevelt's injection of the fuel of public expenditure had started it moving, but—as events would soon show—a far bigger injection was required to keep it from falling back into idleness.

In 1938, after five years of efforts to cure it, the slump seemed to worsen. Unemployment rose to ten million. Roosevelt might have left Washington after his second term—and history's view of him might be different—had not war begun in 1939 and presented him with new challenges to which he responded brilliantly.

A DARK VICTORY

There were two apt descriptions of Washington in the late thirties. A magazine article called it "America's number one boom town." And some inhabitants coined the phrase "First city worst city." Both were right.

The town benefited from the influx of intelligent people seeking to work in the New Deal Administration, and from the great increase in lobbies—organizations that came to influence legislation. But the attitude toward destitute Negroes continued to be bad.

In 1936 a very damaging rule was made. To keep relief payments down, it was decided in the District of Columbia that no government help would go to any family in which an employable man lived. This meant that a poor Negro family received no assistance as long as the father remained with the family. The rule encouraged fathers to desert families. When mothers then went to work, children were left alone without parents, and the problem of juvenile delinquency which still clings to the city was created.

When a social worker found her job impossible and visited the chairman of the House D.C. Committee to request more relief help, she received an unusually frank answer. The chairman, Representative Ross Collins of Mississippi, said, "If I went along with your ideas, I'd never keep my seat in Congress. My constituents wouldn't stand for spending all that money on Negroes."

In 1939, one event gave promise of change. Marian Anderson, the famous Negro contralto, came to Washington for a singing engagement. An attempt was made to hire Constitution Hall, the stately white marble building near the White House owned by the Daughters of the American Revolution. The D.A.R. refused, stating that the auditorium had already been reserved for other programs. However, public attention was drawn to the "White Artists Only" clause in all its rental contracts. The sponsors of the occasion turned to a white high-school auditorium, which was begrudgingly allowed them.

Marian Anderson singing at the Lincoln Memorial.

Roosevelt's short-tempered Secretary of the Interior, Harold

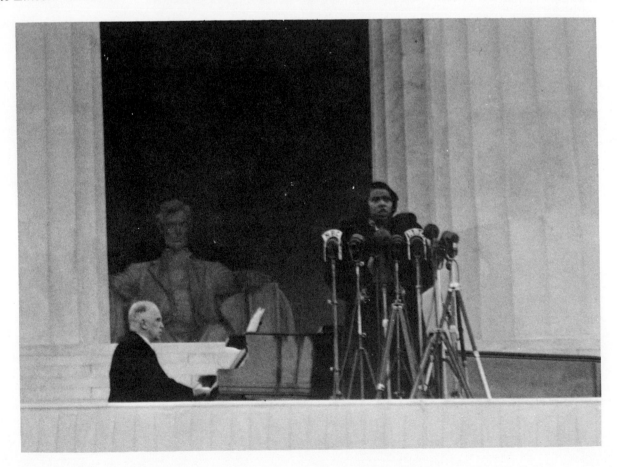

Ickes, heard of the problem. He phoned the sponsors of the concert: They had his permission to use the Lincoln Memorial. So Miss Anderson sang in a majestic setting, with the greatest President looking down on her and a huge audience looking up at her. Negro pride and white sympathy grew together.

In defense of the D.A.R., it should be said that the color clause appeared in most District of Columbia contracts at that time. The D.A.R. never required segregated audiences for any event, and it soon offered its hall for rental to Negro artists. Miss Anderson sang there repeatedly in the 1950s.

But now, in the late thirties, a greater crisis was gathering. It would offer Negroes opportunities; and it would offer America a second chance at greatness.

THE FORCES OF EVIL

Five weeks before Roosevelt's first inauguration a different inauguration was held in Berlin, the capital of Germany. Adolf Hitler, a man of shallow mind and twisted spirit, became Chancellor (Prime Minister) of Germany. Somewhat earlier, Japanese militarists murdered their prime minister and began an invasion of China. Somewhat later, the Italian dictator, Mussolini, invaded Ethiopia in Africa.

Throughout the 1930s, these three nations relentlessly assaulted weaker neighbors one by one. Each new aggression was preceded by shrill campaigns of lies and intimidation. Each conquest was followed by brutality and murder and the filling of prisons with those who dissented. After a while, the three formed an alliance called the "Rome-Berlin-Tokyo Axis." It soon became the gravest threat to liberal, capitalist civilization up to that time.

We have pointed out the failure of the New Deal to cure economic depression. We must now add that its triumphs far surpassed its defeats. Nations all over the world sought to meet their problems of domestic depression by limiting or abolishing freedom at home and by aggression and conquest abroad. But Roosevelt had given democracy deeper meaning in America. He had spread real power more widely among the people. Conservatives who considered him a radical would have to admit that he, more than any man, saved capitalism and made it stronger in its greatest trial.

Roosevelt recognized the menace of the Axis more clearly than any other chief of state. He would, against great difficulties, make Washington the main headquarters for resisting the Axis.

CHAPTER NINE
THE ARSENAL OF DEMOCRACY

EYES THAT SEE NOT

Roosevelt's second Inaugural Address, treating the problems before the nation in 1937, contained not one word about foreign affairs. Yet in the preceding twelve months Italy had invaded Ethiopia; Franco had begun the Spanish Civil War with Nazi and Italian Fascist help; Germany had formally denounced the Versailles Treaty with its restrictions on her rearming; and Japan had plunged deeper into China.

America's disgust with the world that had emerged from war in 1918 now deepened. We refused to acknowledge that its worsening troubles had anything to do with us.

Between 1935 and 1937, Congress passed a series of neutrality laws aimed at keeping America out of any war. A Congressman named Ludlow even introduced an amendment to the Constitution which required a national plebiscite before war could be declared. It failed to win the necessary two-thirds vote, but a clear majority in Congress supported a measure which would have required Americans to hold a national election before defending our soil against an invasion!

The President's worry increased after his inauguration in 1937. To try to mobilize concern, he made a speech proposing that the aggressor nations be "quarantined." The response among the American people was poor. He told a friend, "It is a terrible thing to look over your shoulder when you are trying to lead—and find no one there!"

The attitude of democratic leaders in Europe was no help. In January, 1938, the President asked the Prime Minister of Great Britain, Neville Chamberlain, to join him in holding a conference of free-world leaders to harmonize policies. Chamberlain refused,

"SHH-HH! HE'LL BE QUIET NOW—MAYBE!"

125

*An American comment
on Neville Chamberlain's
policy of "appeasement."*

saying it would interfere with his policy which he called one of
"appeasement" of the dictators. Chamberlain was unfortunately
right when he explained privately, "It is always best to count on
nothing from the Americans but words." The dictators moved
on, undermining one bastion after another that might have been
defended against them.

The mood of Congress was demonstrated in a meeting of Senate
leaders whom the President called to the White House to request
a loosening of the neutrality laws. When he spoke of the possibility
of war, the powerful Senator William Borah answered, "There's not
going to be any war this year. All this hysteria is manufactured and
artificial."

Said the Secretary of State, Cordell Hull, who was also present,
"I wish the Senator would come down to my office and read the
cables."

Answered Borah, "I have sources in Europe that I regard as
more reliable than those of the State Department." Hull fought back

tears of frustration. Within the year, World War II broke out.

The President was particularly disappointed that many young people did not support him. Mrs. Roosevelt arranged a meeting between the President and student leaders at the White House. When he tried to explain the necessity for making defense preparations, the students berated him for being more concerned about national defense than about "social defense." Unable to bear the youthful upbraiding at a moment when France was falling and Britain was isolated, the President said to the shrillest of them, "Young man . . . have you read Carl Sandburg's Lincoln?" The youth said he had not. Roosevelt said, "I think the impression was that Lincoln was a pretty sad man. . . . He was a sad man because he couldn't get it all at once. And nobody can."

In one respect history is a misleading study. Because it is behind us, we know how things turned out in the end. Any picture of the late 1930s is unreal if it does not convey the chill fear of the time, when it seemed that democracy was on the way out and the dictators were going to inherit the earth.

UNCLE SAM'S ADOPTED NEPHEW

He came so often to Washington that he became part of the city's story. He addressed Congress and was cheered. Eventually Con-

Winston Churchill addressing Congress during World War II. On the rostrum behind him: Sam Rayburn, Speaker of the House (right), and Henry Wallace, FDR's third-term Vice President.

gress made him an honorary citizen of the United States, an honor voted before then only to the Marquis de Lafayette for his help in the American Revolution.

When war approached England, he was an ordinary Member of Parliament. He was a veteran of many political wars, in which he had accumulated so many enemies that it seemed certain he had no political future. But he possessed the finest command of the English language of any man alive, and he had a record of being completely right about the dictators.

When the European Alliance collapsed in the spring of 1940—when Norway, Denmark, the Netherlands, Belgium, and France joined Poland in subjugation to Hitler—his political foes still sought to persuade the King to call someone else to lead England. The King knew no one else would be accepted. He called the old bulldog.

"As I went to bed at about 3 A.M.," Winston Churchill later wrote of that long night, "I was conscious of a profound sense of relief. At last I had the authority to give directions over the whole scene. I felt as if I were walking with Destiny, and that all my past life had been but a preparation for this hour."

Across the Atlantic in the White House, Franklin Roosevelt too was conscious of a profound sense of relief. At last he had someone he could work with. With a vigor he had not felt since the peak of the New Deal, the President equipped his neutral nation to act.

He appointed two Republicans to his cabinet, forming a bipartisan coalition. He created the National Defense Research Council to gather all that science had discovered or could discover about building defense. He persuaded Congress to pass a bill drafting young men into the armed forces. The bill passed, but in so heated an atmosphere that one Congressman punched another in the nose. He also let himself be drafted to run and be elected President a third time, in 1940.

American warships cooperated ever more openly with the British against Hitler's U-boats. Congress passed the Lend-Lease Act to enable the British, fighting alone and running out of money, to receive a plentiful flow of American arms without payment. When Russia was attacked by Hitler, the lend-lease program was extended to help the Russians.

The aggressors were growing impatient with this generous nation which supplied guns and equipment to everyone who resisted their attacks. The Japanese finally determined to act. In the early morning of December 7, 1941, they made a surprise air attack on the

Eleanor Roosevelt's satin ballgown for her husband's third inauguration.

American base at Pearl Harbor in Hawaii. It was a grievous blow to American naval power and to American pride and prestige. But the Japanese attack was—in terms of ultimate results—one of the great mistakes in history. Keeping America out of the war would have been a great achievement for the Axis. But the attack on Pearl Harbor swept away all confusions and doubts and illusions and hesitations. It meant the release of a power unbelievable to the Axis—and even to Americans themselves. Only Churchill seemed to have an exact idea of what it meant.

When he heard the news, he phoned Washington.

"Mr. President," he said, "what is this about Japan?"

"It's quite true," answered Roosevelt. "They have attacked Pearl Harbor. We are all in the same boat now."

"It simplifies things," said Churchill.

That same night, Churchill composed a letter to the King. "I have formed the conviction that it is my duty to visit Washington without delay," he said. To himself he made a prophecy of which he was sure even at that early date, with England still hurting from the pain of Hitler's attacks, with so many setbacks still ahead: "So —we have won!"

THE GIANT UNLEASHED

Germany and Italy declared war on the United States promptly after the Japanese attack on Pearl Harbor. The Axis partners then proceeded to win some of the most impressive victories in military history. The lash of defeat caused Washington to strain all the harder to reverse the trend.

To make America, in FDR's words, "the arsenal of democracy," a War Production Board was put to work. It combined managers and scientists and workers into the most productive organization ever known. The Navy set its sights high and asked for 60 vessels in 60 days. It received 67. Roosevelt asked for 45,000 tanks and 60,000 airplanes in a year. He got more.

Unemployment, which had been 10 million in 1939, virtually disappeared by 1944. So great was the demand for labor that industries performed every little service, such as sending a task force of plumbers around to repair leaky faucets in workers' homes, so the workers would lose no time away from work. There was a story that an employer advertised in the papers, "Waitress wanted; will marry."

At the outbreak of war, America possessed fewer arms than

Wartime Washington was at first "defended" with wooden machine guns—here demonstrated by Congressman Harold O. Cooley.

Poland had when the Nazis attacked her—and Germany defeated Poland in sixteen days. Now America became the best-equipped nation ever known, and a huge overflow of equipment went to all Allies.

Some of the goods given to our own 15 million soldiers and 4 million sailors were stamped "Government Issue." According to one story, it was from these initials that American soldiers nicknamed themselves "GIs." Another story says they took the name from the Galvanized Iron garbage cans outside Army messes. In any case, the nation adopted the term.

The GIs were the best-cared-for soldiers ever. For every 8,000 fighting men there were 6,000 service troops to supply them and entertain them and help them when wounded.

In the Civil War more than half the nation's 600,000 casualties died. In this war of much deadlier weapons, fewer than a third of our million casualties died, thanks to immensely better care. During World War II more Americans died in auto accidents than died in combat.

For Americans at home it was a unique experience. The more we converted our resources into food and war materials for use abroad, the better off we became at home. Some commodities in

America were rationed, but compared to any of the European rationing systems, they were still available in abundance. What the New Deal had been too timid to do—spend money on a very large scale—war did. This suggested what might be done in peacetime to end recessions, and the idea was applied by both our political parties after the war.

WASHINGTON AT WAR

The armed forces, once satisfied with a couple of small buildings next to the White House, now needed a large office building. A site was chosen on the Virginia shore of the Potomac near the newly opened National Airport.

President Roosevelt wanted the structure to be a five-sided fortress, with solid walls and no windows, rather like the windowless National Art Gallery on the Mall. It was pointed out to him that if bombs fell near a windowless building, they would blow the walls in. So he agreed to windows.

The result was the Pentagon, finished in 1942, able to house 42,000 workers and to feed 6,000 at a sitting. It covers forty-two acres, the greatest area occupied by any office building in the world.

When it was nearly completed, the President inspected it and found a curious feature. Wherever there were toilets, they numbered four in a row. There being but two sexes, Roosevelt asked why there were four separate toilets. He was told that, naturally, Negro *The Pentagon* men and women would have toilets separate from those for white

men and women. The President ordered the numbers reduced to two.

Segregation persisted in most areas of life, even in the armed services. So a Negro leader, A. Philip Randolph, head of the Union of Sleeping Car Porters, planned a mass march of protest on Washington. President Roosevelt, dealing with a swarm of programs, begged Randolph to call it off, lest it create a bad impression in the world. Randolph suggested that the bad impression would be avoided if segregation were ended. So the President issued the Fair Employment Practices Code, ordering the end of segregation in all industries working for the government. Not all obeyed, but many did, bringing some improvement. Segregation in the armed forces, however, continued until the Korean War.

The demand for labor greatly improved the lot of colored people. In Washington, schools for Negroes began teaching three shifts of pupils per day. As fast as they graduated, they were absorbed in well-paid jobs. By early 1941 there was no Negro unemployment in Washington.

But the federal government continued to pay little attention to the problems of its capital city. The flood of new arrivals, considering themselves temporary citizens, did not contribute to the Community Chest fund for charities. However, when the fund was turned into a war chest for the needy of all Allied nations, especially China, Washington was given a fraction of the proceeds. In this manner District of Columbia charities received more money than ever before, for Americans are very generous to non-Americans.

The housing shortage was severe. As in the city's first year, in 1800, people were often crowded several to a room. The President called off the annual Cherry Blossom Festival to try to keep people out of town. He also continued the blackout, prohibiting lights on Washington's streets, long after all other cities had returned to bright lights.

BUREAUCRACY

The magazine *Readers' Digest* found the workings of the big new army of government office workers, the bureaucracy, so fascinating that it published a regular section entitled "Washington Wonderland," in which it recounted stories, some embroidered, some true, about inefficiency.

One story told of the frustrated Japanese spy who reported back

In August, 1941, four months before America was at war, Roosevelt went to Argentia Bay in Newfoundland to meet Churchill on board a warship. They issued the Atlantic Charter, a statement of their peace aims.

Many summit meetings followed. One of the most important was in 1943 in Teheran, the capital of Persia, where Roosevelt and Churchill met the Russian dictator, Stalin, for the first time. Among many agreements was one to adopt a term suggested by Roosevelt and create a United Nations organization to try to keep world peace when war ended.

In the summer of 1944, a conference to plan that organization was held in Washington, in the magnificent old Georgetown mansion of Dumbarton Oaks. (It had once been the home of John C. Calhoun, Vice President of the United States, and was now owned by Harvard University.)

As America had rejected the League of Nations after World War I, the big question was whether the country would reject the United Nations now.

In contrast to Wilson, who had planned and negotiated peace alone, Roosevelt involved leaders of Congress as much as possible. One of these was Senator Arthur Vandenberg of Michigan, leader of the isolationists. After the outbreak of war in Europe, Vandenberg had said, "This so-called war is nothing but about twenty-five people and propaganda." Later, however, on an official visit in London, watching people under a Nazi buzz bomb attack, the isolationist Senator was visibly shaken.

Now, on January 10, 1945, Vandenberg stood in the Senate and said, "I have always been frankly one of those who believed in our own self-reliance. . . . But I do not believe any nation hereafter can immunize itself by its own exclusive action. . . . I want the maximum American cooperation. . . . I think that American interest requires it."

When he sat down, something unusual happened. Applause burst out from his fellow Senators, and spread up into the visitors' galleries. The Senate—which had refused to let America join the League of Nations—voted to have America join the U.N. The vote was 88 to 2.

THE DAY THE MOON AND THE STARS FELL

Harry S (a decorative middle initial, standing for nothing) Truman of Missouri was a plain man who served as a captain, then a major, in the First World War; failed as part owner of a clothing shop in a postwar recession; but became a very good U.S. Senator. In the Second World War, he headed a "watchdog committee" of Congress that investigated our gigantic war expenditures in order to prevent waste. He visited most major war plants and saved the nation a good deal of money.

When Roosevelt ran for President the fourth time in 1944, he sought to keep his current Vice President, Henry A. Wallace. Political leaders rebelled against supporting the occasionally brilliant but often erratic Wallace. Then Roosevelt proposed James Byrnes of South Carolina, who had served in high places in all three branches of the government. Labor and Negroes refused to support a Southerner. So Roosevelt proposed Truman as his third choice. No one objected, and Truman became Vice President.

Roosevelt made almost no use of his Vice Presidents and told them nothing. His first Vice President, John N. Garner of Texas, said—in his vivid if earthy way—that the job "ain't worth a bucket of warm spit." Truman as Vice President had almost no contact with FDR, so he spent most of his time in his old haunt, the Capitol.

On the afternoon of April 12, 1945, he was sitting in Speaker Sam Rayburn's office when a telephone call begged him to come to the White House quickly. He raced there and was received by Mrs. Roosevelt.

"Harry," she said, "the President is dead." Like others, Truman had noticed that the President had grown thin and suffered from a bad cough and had deep dark circles under his eyes. But there was a kind of unspoken assumption that FDR, having been there so

In the President's oval White House office, beneath FDR's portrait of Woodrow Wilson, Harry S. Truman is hurriedly sworn in as President. Second from left is Frances Perkins, FDR's Secretary of Labor. Third from left is Henry L. Stimson, Secretary of War; an hour after this ceremony he informed President Truman of a powerful new weapon.

long, would always be there. Now he had died of a hemorrhage in his overworked brain.

Truman asked if he could do anything for Mrs. Roosevelt. She answered, "Is there anything *we* can do for *you*? You are the one in trouble now."

FDR's funeral cortege, on Constitution Avenue.

To reporters Truman said, "Pray for me, boys. The moon, the stars and all the planets fell on me."

BLOODY IWO

By the time of the invasion of Hitler's Europe, Allied aircraft, mainly produced in America, had blasted Hitler's air force nearly to extinction. The Allies had a 30 to 1 air superiority.

In the Pacific, a long process of island-hopping brought American airplanes within bombing distance of Tokyo. But the flight to and from Tokyo took sixteen hours, and American bombers often crashed into the sea for lack of fuel. It was decided to invade and take the ugly, pear-shaped island of Iwo Jima, a little over 500 miles from Tokyo, in order to have a way station where bombers could land. A base on Iwo would also allow the bombers to be covered by short-range fighter planes.

The invasion was one of the bloodiest battles Americans have ever fought, costing the Marines 5,500 dead and 17,000 wounded. It laid Tokyo open to devastation. We mention it in a book about Washington because of a photograph taken by Associated Press photographer Joe Rosenthal.

The Marines took the highest peak on Iwo Jima, and on a length of Japanese pipe raised a small American flag. The flag was too small to be seen, so a larger one was brought from a landing craft. Photographer Rosenthal saw the large flag being carried up the mountain, followed it, and snapped a picture of six Marines raising it.

His photograph caused a sensation. It became the most famous photo of the war, or, indeed, the most famous of any time or occasion. It was used as a poster for a War Loan campaign, as a postage stamp, and for many other purposes.

Its most remarkable use was as the model for the largest bronze statue ever made. In 1954, on the Virginia side of the river in Washington, the Iwo Jima Memorial to the U.S. Marines was unveiled.

Rosenthal's famous photograph (left) and the monument based on it.

The height of the men was multiplied by five to 32 feet, and the flag to 60 feet. Though from the river the memorial has a drab background of modern apartments, it is one of the most impressive monuments in the capital.

THE FAT BOY

In August of 1939, two professors—both speaking English with thick accents, both chased out of Europe by Hitler—sought out a third exile, Albert Einstein, at his retreat on Long Island. The two were named Szilard and Teller, and were not famous. Einstein was famous. So they sought his signature to a letter they were sending to the President of the United States. Einstein signed it.

The letter said in part, "It may become possible to set up a nuclear chain reaction in a large mass of uranium. . . . This new phenomenon would also lead to the construction of bombs . . . extremely powerful bombs."

The three scientists were surer than their letter sounded of the feasibility of creating nuclear weapons strong enough to wipe out whole cities. They were afraid that Hitler was well on the way to creating such bombs, and if he succeeded first, the world would be at his mercy. They sought to persuade the President of the United States to order such weapons made first.

The letter was given to Alexander Sachs, a man of wealth and a patron of scholars. Sachs was a frequent adviser to the President. On October 12, 1939, Sachs saw the President, handed him the letter, and tried to explain it. It was characteristic of Roosevelt that he did not dwell on any one subject long, but darted from one topic to another. Perhaps that habit of mind is necessary to a President, who must decide a host of different questions each day. Anyhow, this subject was too fantastic to be understood quickly, so Roosevelt dismissed it.

That night Sachs stayed in the Carlton Hotel, not far from the White House. Here is his story, as told to Robert Jungk: "I didn't sleep a wink. . . . I paced restlessly to and fro . . . or tried to sleep sitting in a chair. . . . Three or four times, I believe, between eleven in the evening and seven in the morning, I left the hotel, to the porter's amazement, and went across to the park. There I sat on a bench and meditated. . . .

"Quite suddenly, like an inspiration, the right idea came to me. I returned to the hotel, took a shower, and shortly afterwards called once more at the White House."

Roosevelt asked, "What bright idea have you got now?"

Sachs answered, "All I want to do is to tell you a story." And he proceeded to tell the President how Robert Fulton had proposed to Napoleon the idea of a steam-driven ship. A ship without sails seemed so ridiculous that Napoleon refused to pay attention. He lost his wars.

The story had its effect. Roosevelt jotted some notes on a piece of paper. Then he called in an aide, General Watson, known to him as "Pa." He said, "Pa, this requires action," and he handed Watson the paper. That is how one of the largest decisions in history was made.

The quest for a nuclear explosive moved slowly at first, then gained speed and magnitude. It was called the "Manhattan Project." In an amazingly gossipy nation, and in an amazingly gossipy city, two billion dollars were spent on the project, and no one found out. Neither MacArthur commanding in the Pacific, nor Eisenhower in Europe, knew of it. Neither did Vice President Truman. He was first told of it an hour after taking the oath as President.

When the war in Europe was over and President Truman was in conference with the Allies in Potsdam, outside Berlin, he was given a memo telling him that the first atomic explosion had been produced in the New Mexico desert. Churchill said, "This is the Second Coming, in wrath." Truman sent an ultimatum to the Japanese saying they must surrender or face "prompt and utter destruction."

Back home in the White House, Truman was told America possessed a total of two atom bombs. The first was a long bomb, code-named the "Lean Boy." The second, which was rotund, was called the "Fat Boy." Truman ordered them moved to the Pacific and used any time in August.

Truman has been criticized for this decision. But his supporters argued that with the information he then possessed, his decision was justified. The Japanese did not respond to his ultimatum. He faced the responsibility for a surface invasion of Japan which would have cost hundreds of thousands of American casualties. He also had to consider that a number of bombing raids with conventional bombs had devastated Berlin and Tokyo as badly as a single atomic bomb could damage its target.

On August 8, 1945, the first nuclear bomb used in war was dropped on Japan's Chicago—Hiroshima. A few days later the second was dropped on Nagasaki. The Japanese sued for peace. On September 2, 1945, the biggest war in history ended.

Ironically, Hitler had never been close to making atomic weapons. So the original reason for launching the project was mistaken.

Military police with joyful crowds outside the White House on V-J Day, the end of the war with Japan. Four months earlier there had been similar rejoicing on V-E Day, the end of the war in Europe.

THE LONELY SUMMIT

Those who governed the nation in Washington had decided they were duty-bound to avoid a repetition of America's behavior after the First World War. They believed Washington would be one of several world capitals that would organize the peace. However, they did not expect it to be the *only* Western capital to bear that responsibility.

But in the war's aftermath, one former leading capital after another was forced to admit it could no longer play its old role. Industries were worn out. National finances were exhausted. Fields had been overused. People were tired. As a great power capital, Washington found itself nearly alone.

Its discomfort was increased by the possession of the most terrible weapon ever conceived. With this weapon Washington controlled for several years a fire power—the ultimate ability to destroy an opponent—nearly a million times greater than that of any other nation.

L'Enfant's hamlet, now overgrown, possessed a power and a responsibility such as no capital in history had ever had. It was not happy about it. But it faced up to it.

CHAPTER TEN
A CITY ON A LONELY SUMMIT

A NEW KIND OF WAR

In 1832, when Andrew Jackson began his journey to Washington to be inaugurated, a distinguished Frenchman approached the same destination from Paris. His name was Alexis de Tocqueville. After touring the new nation, he returned home and wrote a brilliant study, *Democracy in America*.

At one point in his commentary he compared two little-known peoples of that time: "I allude to the Russians and the Americans. Both have grown up unnoticed . . . while the attention of mankind was directed elsewhere. . . . Their starting point is different and their courses are not the same; yet each of them seems marked out by the will of Heaven to sway the destinies of half the globe."

For a century his prophecy remained unfulfilled. In 1939 when World War II began, the great powers that determined war and peace did not include Russia or America. Both were isolated from the world. But in that war the power of Paris, then of Berlin and Tokyo, was destroyed. Soon after the war London abdicated from power because of exhaustion. Thus finally the prediction of Alexis de Tocqueville was fulfilled: Only Moscow and Washington remained as powerful world capitals, and each did sway the destinies of half the globe.

Because their rivalry dominated every aspect of Washington's life for two decades, the attitudes of the two governments deserve a little explanation.

America ended the war in a mood of constructive innocence. On his desk President Truman displayed a toy gun and a toy plow to symbolize the transition he aimed to carry through. In foreign affairs, the President, Congress, and the people hoped that the war-

Signing the United Nations charter, San Francisco, 1945.

time alliance would endure. America and Russia, working together in the United Nations, would revive the other Allies and build a prosperous world.

The United States was more troubled than pleased at her monopoly of nuclear weapons. The Baruch Plan was proposed: All nuclear materials would be owned by the U.N., and America would destroy all her weapons and make no more. Russia rejected the plan.

The President and Congress yielded to maternal pressures and let the great American armed forces disintegrate. It had been planned to demobilize around 5 million men in the first year after the war. In fact, close to 9 million were released. "It was not a demobilization," General Marshall complained, "it was a rout." General Wedemeyer wrote, "America fought the war like a football game, after which the winner leaves the field and celebrates."

U.N. aid was begun, the United States paying the most, Russia receiving the most. A flow of reparations to Russia from West Germany began. Later, when Marshall Plan aid was begun, it too was offered to Russia.

Russia's attitude was very different from America's. She had been invaded and devastated often. So her rulers determined to use the sudden weakness of the rest of Europe to grab control of neighboring nations and build them into a protective buffer. Having known and practiced nothing for centuries but brutal and arbitrary dictatorship, Moscow was morbidly suspicious of everyone and nearly impossible to cooperate with.

In addition, there was the factor of ideology. In their revolution in 1918, the Russian rulers adopted an ideology based on the ideas of a nineteenth-century German, Karl Marx. According to Russian Marxism, the capitalist nations of the West were degenerate, and the Communists—Russia primarily—were destined to inherit the earth. Under capitalism, depressions like that of the 1930s would recur and grow worse. The workers in the West would be exploited by their employers until they revolted and seized their governments. Meanwhile, the capitalist nations would fight terrible wars with one another in order to seize or hold colonies.

Actually, none of this happened after World War II. There was no depression. The workers became pillars rather than wreckers of capitalism. Far from fighting to gain colonies, those nations that possessed them gave them up.

Still, the dark medieval mind of Stalin, the Russian tyrant, was dominated by these Marxist expectations. He felt it his duty to seize control of nations and spare them the horrors of capitalism. By bluffing and bullying, by ordering local Communist parties to undermine and subvert their governments, and even—as in Greece—by fomenting civil war, Russia sought to extend her influence.

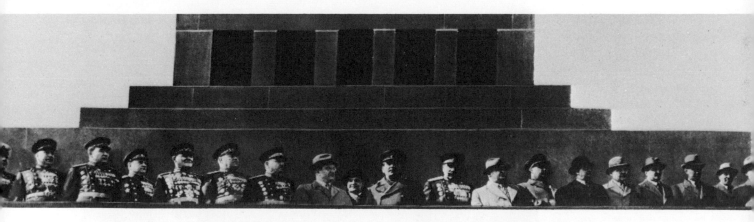

Americans were disappointed and soon became angry. But Washington was at a loss for a way to meet and block this new kind of indirect war. It helped a little when someone at last found a name for it: Bernard Baruch—the financier who had organized American industry for President Wilson—had to make a speech in Columbia, South Carolina, on April 16, 1947. He induced a friend, the gifted journalist Herbert Bayard Swope, to write the speech. Swope created a phrase, and in his speech, Baruch named the conflict the Cold War.

May Day in Moscow, 1947: Josef Stalin and other Russian leaders reviewing Soviet troops from their vantage point on Lenin's tomb.

A generation has passed, and no one has yet found a better name for the trying conflict that now became Washington's chief concern.

WASHINGTON TAKES COMMAND

What to do? The effort to answer that question provoked a kind of golden age in the Department of State. In the long period of isolationism, the department had minor functions. In our two conspicuous breakouts from isolationism, two strong Presidents—Wilson and F. D. Roosevelt—ran foreign affairs without much reference to the department. But the new situation of the Cold War called for hard thought and specialized work by many people.

In 1947, the State Department was moved out of the huge granite building next door to the White House into a vast, modernistic warren in the "Foggy Bottom" area of the city, just south of Georgetown. President Truman endowed the department with prestige by appointing General George Marshall as Secretary of State. Marshall chose as his Undersecretary Dean Gooderham Acheson, who later succeeded him as Secretary.

Under Truman, Marshall, and Acheson, Washington produced, in a mere two years, as remarkable a succession of acts of creative diplomacy as ever came out of any capital.

President Truman appointed two outstanding Secretaries of State: George Marshall (left) and Dean Acheson (right).

On February 24, 1947, it began. The British Ambassador called on Acheson and brought shocking news. Britain was too exhausted by war to continue supporting Greece and Turkey, both under severe Communist pressure. Britain would have to withdraw support by March 31, little more than a month away. After that both countries would surely fall behind the Iron Curtain.

Acheson and his staff advised the President to throw America's resources into the breach. Truman called Congressional leaders to the White House and told them of his wish. "If that's what you want, Mr. President," Senator Vandenberg said of this unprecedented request, "there's only one way to get it. That is to make a personal appearance before Congress and scare the hell out of the country."

Truman went before Congress. His speech was carried by radio to the nation. He said it was his policy to support Greece and Turkey—and any other nation menaced by the Communists. His statement was called the Truman Doctrine. *The New York Times* called it "a revolution in U.S. foreign policy more notable even than American participation in the U.N."

Congress appropriated the money and on May 22, 1947, Truman signed the bill putting America, in effect, in charge of Western defense in the Cold War.

Containment

Instead of meeting individual challenges as they came, the State Department determined to provide itself with a general policy to suit any case that might arise. The statement of a grand design appeared in the July, 1947, issue of *Foreign Affairs* magazine and was signed simply "by X." The initial disguised George M. Kennan, Chief of Policy Planning in the State Department. The article set forth the policy of "containment." This meant blocking all Russian probes patiently until in good time the Russians found the effort too strenuous. One of the great policy papers of all time, it did much to clarify the thinking of Americans.

The Marshall Plan

It soon became clear that Greece and Turkey were not the only nations in trouble. In the winter of 1946–47, the strain of two world wars became evident as all the former great powers of Western Europe verged on economic collapse. Communist parties went to work, and it appeared that the whole area might fall to them.

The State Department worked up a proposal and on June 4, 1947, Secretary Marshall announced it: There would be no more piecemeal relief; instead the United States would supply whatever help all Europe—including Russia and her puppet or satellite countries—needed for full economic recovery.

The European nations met in Paris to consider the offer. Russia and her satellites tried to break up the meeting; failing, they walked out.

Truman told Congress the whole plan would cost 17 billion dollars, or 4 billion for the first year. Congress was shocked. But the Communist seizure of Czechoslovakia and the threat of a Communist victory in the elections of weakened Italy caused Congress to pass the Marshall Plan by a vote of 69 to 7. The date Europe was rescued was April 2, 1948.

NATO

One more step remained: to build a line of steel against military threats, behind which the Marshall Plan could do its work.

Berlin airlift: An American plane bringing food into the blockaded city.

Again Russia spurred an unwilling Congress to act with vigor. She threw a blockade around the Western sectors of Berlin to try to force the three Western nations out. Not having adequate land forces to break the blockade, the Western nations flew supplies in. By airlift they saved West Berlin from cold and hunger. The Russians eventually abandoned their fruitless effort. But the Allies had by then determined to create a force to prevent future acts of the kind. The North Atlantic Treaty was signed in Washington under Acheson's guidance. An integrated Western armed force was begun. The famous victor of World War II, General Eisenhower, left civilian life to take over its command.

Point Four

The last major creative act of this period was the plan to extend aid to the host of new nations, created from the dissolving empires once run by Europe. In a major address, President Truman included it as the fourth point he wanted to make—so "Point Four" became famous.

Point Four aid is still with us. It is now called foreign aid. It has not worked as well as the other Washington creations of the time. But if some thoughtful newcomer to the State Department can reformulate it to make it effective, he will earn mankind's praise.

For the widening gap in wealth between rich and poor nations in the world is one of our most dangerous problems.

Each of the creative acts of the 1947–49 period was subject to debate and dissent. But in general they have worked. Greece and Turkey were rescued. Western Europe soon enjoyed a higher standard of living than ever before. And there have been signs that Russia is tiring of the quest for world domination.

There have been men as good or better in the State Department both before and after this time. But conditions were right for creative diplomacy in the late forties. Like most golden ages in history, this one was not acknowledged as such until it was over.

S. FOR SURPRISE

Harry S. Truman had a harder time in the White House than most Presidents. A reluctant Congress frustrated his Fair Deal program to make America a better place to live. Organized labor went on a rampage. In 1946, strikes caused the record loss of 107 million

President Truman in 1947 added a balcony to the South Portico of the White House.

and journalists chose him as "the best" of the then 96 Senators.

Now came a strange interlude. It happens sometimes that a Senator becomes so involved with the nation's interests that a demagogue can accuse him of neglecting his own state. That happened to young La Follette. In 1946, he was displaced as Senator from Wisconsin by a man the political scientists and reporters soon voted "the worst" of the 96 Senators.

The worst Senator was Joseph Raymond McCarthy of Appleton, Wisconsin. As some people are color-blind, the black-jowled McCarthy was ethics-blind. Right and wrong, truth and falsehood, were meaningless words to him. In political campaigns, he gave various dates for his birth to fit whatever impression of youth or maturity he thought would help him. As a local judge, he destroyed part of the records of a case when his judgment was appealed to a higher court. He pocketed very large sums of money for which there was no record in his income tax returns. He ran for the Senate as "Tail Gunner Joe," showing photos of himself manning a gun in World War II, and boasting of his combat experiences. Occasionally he limped and complained of "ten pounds of shrapnel" buried in his leg. In fact, he had served in the war as a Marine desk officer and had no shrapnel at all in him.

Senator Joseph R. McCarthy

By 1950, McCarthy began to worry that his unimpressive record in the Senate would prevent his reelection. At a dinner in Washington with a businessman and two teacher-priests from Georgetown University, he asked them to suggest issues on which he might run for reelection. They mentioned several, including Communism. "That's it," said McCarthy, who had never cared much about Communism and knew little about it. "The government is full of Communists. We can hammer away at them." His dinnermates repudiated him some months later when it became clear how he intended to use the issue.

When the Lincoln's Birthday speechmaking tours were assigned to Republican Senators, McCarthy was sent to Wheeling, West Virginia. In his speech there he waved a piece of paper at his audience and said, "I have here in my hand a list of two hundred and five [persons] that were known to the Secretary of State as being members of the Communist Party and who nevertheless are still working and shaping the policy of the State Department."

He later acknowledged that the paper was a letter dealing with an entirely different subject. In other speeches he changed the number of "known Communists in the State Department" from 205 to 81 and then to 57.

On his return to Washington, no one was more surprised than
McCarthy himself to find he had become a national figure. He had
struck a sensitive nerve in the nation. The puzzling Cold War had.
distressed Americans. Then in 1949 the distress turned to fear: In
August an American airplane carrying sensitized plates returned
to its base in the Far East to find the plates streaked. They were
sent to Washington for interpretation, and President Truman was
enabled to announce that Russia had just exploded its first atomic
bomb. Americans agreed with Dr. Harold Urey, winner of the
Nobel Prize, that the only thing worse than one nation having an
atomic bomb was two nations having it.

By October of the same year, there was another blow. The
Chinese Communists completed their seizure of all of China.
The nation that had fought as an ally of the Americans in
World War II was now lost to a hostile force whose methods were
frightening.

Then in 1950, the same month that McCarthy decided to adopt
the issue of Communism, two events dominated the news. First, in
Britain the physicist Klaus Fuchs was arrested for giving atomic
secrets to the Russians. And, second, wholly unrelated to it, the
Hiss case came to a climax. Alger Hiss, a handsome, well-educated
American who had previously worked in the State Department, was
convicted of perjury in a trial in which it was said that he had been
a Communist in the 1930s.

In the minds of many Americans, confusion and fear turned to
hysteria. It became easy to believe that the Red tide was advancing
because of treason within the U.S. government. It took a McCarthy,
unembarrassed by facts, to shout it and win attention.

In June, 1950, came another blow to the nation. The North
Korean Communists, equipped by Russia, invaded South Korea.
President Truman made another of his great decisions. He ordered
American troops from Japan into Korea to turn back the invaders.
The U.N. voted to support him, and fifteen other member nations
sent troops. Now, rising American casualties helped McCarthy
sustain emotions.

Money from donors large and small poured in to finance
McCarthy's "crusade." A network of frightened government
employees supplied him with "information" about their co-workers.

Senator Millard Tydings of Maryland headed a subcommittee
which investigated McCarthy's original charges. After a long study,
the investigators called them "a fraud and a hoax." McCarthy then
determined to "get" Tydings. In the 1950 elections, he poured

money and men into Maryland. McCarthy's followers broke many election laws and some moral ones. They distributed a photograph supposedly showing Tydings in friendly conversation with the chief of the U.S. Communist Party; actually it was a composite of two separate photographs. The result was that Tydings was defeated.

McCarthy was also given credit for the defeat of several other Senators. Many who were elected were thought to owe their success to him. The worst Senator had become a power. Policy-making was paralyzed as government officials feared to make decisions McCarthy might brand as pro-Communist. Politics was poisoned by his charge that the Roosevelt and Truman Administrations had been "twenty years of treason."

But McCarthy carried within himself the seeds of his own destruction. In 1952, Republicans returned to power in the White House and on Capitol Hill. With no positive plans or principles, McCarthy could only attack, recklessly. He now included the Republicans' first year back in power in his attack, charging that there had been "twenty-*one* years of treason." Also he launched a ridiculous investigation of the Army, threatening its morale—the last thing a genuine anti-Communist would wish. At long last in December, 1954, a long-suffering Senate voted 67 to 22 to censure his conduct. His influence withered, and as it did his health worsened. In 1957 he died of a liver ailment. At the end some people were astonished to discover that during the years of his ascendancy, all his revelations and threats and charges and lists had uncovered the existence of exactly 0 (for zero) Communists in the U.S. government.

THE LAST OF H.S.T.

Harry Truman was a landmark President. Under him, a course in foreign affairs was staked out. From this course no successor has varied much, and none has added anything essentially new to it. The course was a middle-road one between those Americans who felt that we should yield to our adversary in a world grown too perilous and other Americans who argued that we should put a stop to the Cold War by transforming it into a hot war. Truman began the difficult task of seeking the right mixture of firmness with conciliation in each successive crisis.

His last years in the White House were tortured. The war in Korea dragged on and was called by his opponents "Truman's War." And he suffered a bruising head-on conflict with his great but egotistic military commander, General MacArthur.

General MacArthur had led American forces in the Pacific to victory in the Second World War. He had then presided over the recovery of Japan and the transformation of that aggressive power into a friendly and democratic nation, an achievement of great moment. But he had acquired a taste for making policy, which is forbidden to soldiers under our republican form of government. Truman repeatedly asked MacArthur to desist from issuing policy pronouncements about the war in Korea. MacArthur paid no attention. So, in the last of his great decisions, Truman removed the general from command.

MacArthur returned from the Far East to a nation in a high state of excitement. Truman was being burned in effigy all over the country. In Washington, Congressmen talked to reporters of plans to impeach the President. MacArthur arrived at National Airport to one of the biggest and noisiest receptions the capital had ever seen. He went to Constitution Hall and briefly addressed the D.A.R. The secretary of that organization called his visit probably the most important event in the history of the hall. It was moved and voted to strike the word "probably" from the minutes.

At Congress's invitation, MacArthur appeared in the Capitol to make his farewell address to both houses. It was a moving, if purple, speech. It ended: "When I joined the Army, even before the turn of this century, it was the fulfillment of all my boyish hopes and dreams. . . . The hopes and dreams have long since vanished, but I still remember the refrain of one of the most popular barracks ballads of that day, which proclaimed proudly that old soldiers never die; they just fade away. And like the old soldier of that ballad, I now close my military career and just fade away, an old soldier who tried to do his duty as God gave him the light to see that duty. Good-bye."

Later investigation showed that every leading military figure in America agreed with Truman and thought MacArthur wrong. In time the American public came to agree.

But this incident was the last blow to Truman's career in politics. His Gallup poll rating—the percentage of Americans who thought he was doing a good job—fell to 23. No other President had fallen below 50. An amendment to the Constitution had just been passed permitting a President only two terms in office. Congress had thought it only polite to exempt Truman from the rule, as it was passed during his tenure. Still, under the circumstances, Truman feared he would drag his party to defeat. He was weary of strife, and he decided not to run again.

General MacArthur, though deprived of his command, received a standing ovation from Congress.

It was with great sadness that reporters waved him good-bye at Union Station. His phalanxes of aides were gone, and the swarm of secret servicemen who had hovered around him for seven years had received other assignments. Somewhere in his luggage he took with him the little sign that he had kept on his desk: "The Buck Stops Here." That was a good short description of the spirit of the Truman Presidency.

THE HEALER

The wrench of adjusting to internationalism in a time of confusion and unusual peril had left the nation disunited and the politics of Washington poisoned with recriminations.

At this moment the Republicans succeeded—where Democrats had failed—in persuading General Eisenhower to drop his NATO command and come home to be their candidate for the Presidency.

From his boyhood in Texas and Kansas, "Ike," as he was universally called, had been immensely popular. But well into middle age his career was disappointing to him. In the 1920s and 1930s, when soldiers were not highly regarded, he was stuck at the rank of major for sixteen years, and considered leaving the Army for private business. When war broke out in Europe, there was a sudden demand for officers who could command the respect of large bodies of troops. And there was a special need for commanders who could persuade officers of different nations to work together—for military men can be as temperamental and jealous as actors. Ike proved exceptionally able in both respects.

The story is that General Marshall put Eisenhower in charge of planning a coalition war in Europe. When Ike presented his plan, Marshall said, "Are you satisfied with it?"

"Yes," answered the new two-star general (temporary).

"Fine," said Marshall, "because these are the orders you are to operate under; *you* are in command." Thus began Ike's rapid progress to the rank of five-star general (permanent).

At the end of the war, he was not merely America's favorite citizen, but also the world's. The British presented him with a castle in Scotland. The Germans, whom he had crushed, cheered and celebrated him. When he finally agreed to run for President, there could be no doubt about the outcome.

THE REUNITED STATES

The first Republican administration since Hoover left the Presidency twenty years earlier took over Washington in 1953 and promised drastic changes in policy. At home it promised to cut government spending and balance the federal budget. To do this, Eisenhower chose a conservative Cabinet of "eight millionaires and a plumber." The plumber—the Secretary of Labor—soon quit.

Abroad, Ike's aggressive Secretary of State, John Foster Dulles, promised an end to Truman's policy of containment. Instead he would "liberate" the Communist satellites from Russian domination. And if the Communists probed outward again, he would hit them with "massive retaliation" with nuclear weapons.

But the facts of life soon weakened these promises, and the Eisenhower Administration gradually found itself forced into grooves carved by FDR at home and by Truman in foreign affairs.

At home, there were three small recessions within eight years. So Eisenhower began expanding government spending once again. His two terms in office accumulated the biggest budget deficit of any peacetime administration in history. Far from reducing welfare programs, Eisenhower asked for more than Truman had got. And he created a new Cabinet office—the awkwardly named Department of Health, Education, and Welfare—to administer the programs.

In foreign affairs, following Secretary Dulles' promise of liberation, the East Germans rose against their Communist rulers. Later, the Hungarian people did the same. In both cases Dulles returned to the Truman policy—which was, in essence, to agree tacitly to a line through Europe which we would not let the Russians cross to menace Western Europe, but which we would not cross to menace Eastern Europe. The Russians suppressed both uprisings.

When the French got into trouble in their rebellious colony in Indochina, they asked Dulles for some "massive retaliation" to defeat the Communist rebels. He rejected the French request. The Truman policy of firmness, always tempered with restraint and caution, had become the Republican policy too.

At Andrews Air Force Base near Washington, Chairman Khrushchev shielded his eyes from the sun during President Eisenhower's greeting.

However, the long effort at "containing" the new Russian empire began in these years to bear fruit. The Russian tyrant Stalin died, and was replaced by the much less tyrannical Khrushchev. Khrushchev made a speech to his fellow Communists, a devastating attack on Stalin, revealing that all that Russia's enemies had said about the dictator's methods and aims had been accurate. A considerable liberalizing of Russian society ensued. Twice in the Eisenhower years, the leaders of the three main Western nations met with the Russian chief in summit conferences. One day the world was treated by television to a unique sight in Washington: the Russian dictator, Khrushchev, descending from his airplane to be met by the American President. The leading Communist had come to tour the leading liberal capitalist nation. Rather unwillingly, Khrushchev's eyes were opened to the wealth and power, and the friendliness, of the American nation. Unhappily, he interpreted the friendliness as softness. Americans, he would say later, were "too liberal to fight," and that thought was to lead him into a desperate error, which will be discussed in the next chapter.

When the Eisenhower years ended in January of 1961, they were subject to many criticisms. But when virtues and faults were balanced against one another, the net result was a considerable achievement: The disunion of the nation had been ended, and Washington's politics had been purged of poison.

A GIANT CITY

After other wars Washington's population had declined. After World War II it continued to grow. The Washington metropolitan area, overflowing far into Virginia and Maryland, soon contained more than 2 million inhabitants. Projections suggested there would be 5 million by the end of the century. Washington had become the ninth biggest American city and was growing faster than any other.

Big Business, Big Labor and Big Journalism set up large permanent offices there. George Washington's dream of a commercial city was finally realized as industries—mainly electronics firms—set up plants in the suburbs. Among Washington's many advantages as a place to live was the fact that it was depression-proof. Whenever a recession struck the nation, activity in Washington increased in order to end it.

Of all the newcomers the largest group were Negroes from the South. In the ten years from 1950 to 1960, the Negro proportion of inhabitants of the District of Columbia rose from 35 percent to

54 percent. Washington became the only city outside Africa with a Negro majority.

Yet it was still governed by the District of Columbia committees of Congress, dominated by rural Southern Congressmen who did not appropriate adequate funds for education and welfare.

A political scientist, Professor Royce Hanson, said it was not a government but an "ungovernment." Said *Architectural Forum* magazine, "For accuracy's sake, today's speeches about the glories of our Democracy should always be followed by the words, 'except in Washington.' The fact that those who live in the seat of Democracy do not enjoy its basic prerogatives is, quite literally, incredible."

Thus Washington had the worst municipal government in the nation. But the existence of a permanent federal establishment there offered better opportunities to educated Negroes than they could find anywhere else in the nation. For example, the median Negro income in the nation was $3,000. In Washington it was nearly $5,000.

The second government located in Washington—the federal government of the United States—improved in the years after World War II. For a while it looked as though Congress would be swamped. About 10,000 bills were introduced each year. But Senator Robert La Follette, Jr., and Congressman Mike Monroney of Oklahoma carried out a thoroughgoing reform of Congress, eliminating 17 Senate and 29 House committees, but increasing the staff and simplifying procedures so that Congress could meet its workload.

Laws provided the President with new staffs to keep him abreast of national and world affairs. The White House staff, which numbered 40 under Hoover, would under Kennedy number 1200.

Oddly, the total numbers on the federal payroll decreased. Many functions were streamlined, requiring fewer people in unskilled jobs. Some functions were let out to private enterprise—for example, the planning of Air Force missiles, and many projects in the War on Poverty.

One happy increase was two stars on the flag: Under Eisenhower, Alaska and Hawaii were made states and admitted to the Union, bringing the total of states to fifty and the total of Senators to one hundred.

Any change for the better may bring some new disadvantage too. The turn of America from isolationism to internationalism brought a concern about the world—and an indifference to our own nation.

Congress paid little attention to domestic problems, while it would vote almost any appropriation for defense or foreign affairs. Admiral Hyman Rickover once expressed the belief that if the Russians were to say they were going to Hades, Congress would vote ten billion dollars to get there first.

The indifference to domestic affairs showed even in the architecture of the capital city. While Congress voted funds for the most daring architecture in our embassies abroad—where they would be compared to Russian embassies—it allowed only the safest and plainest buildings to be erected in Washington. Looking at the results, a visitor said, "Washington is surely the worst ravaged of the wartime capitals—not by bombs but by builders."

To many critics, the chief offender was the newly appointed Capitol Architect, J. George Stewart, who was not an architect but an engineer. With the support of a few Congressional leaders he tore down the old sandstone east front of the Capitol, where Presidents were inaugurated. He replaced it with a marble replica, moved farther outward in order to create more office space. Later, over a storm of protests in Congress, he prepared to do the same with the west front of the Capitol. Also he presided over the construction of big, uninteresting, exorbitantly costly Congressional office buildings, which today crowd the view of the Capitol itself.

At the end of the 1950s, two major changes were about to take place in Washington. The federal government, indifferent to its home city for most of its history, was to take a sudden new interest and launch some of the finest improvements since Pierre L'Enfant first designed the capital. And the lonely summit on which Washington was perched in a very dangerous world was to be—after one of the worst crises of the age—somewhat less lonely and less dangerous.

Mrs. Dwight D. Eisenhower's dress of silk with rhinestones.

CHAPTER ELEVEN
WASHINGTON IN OUR TIME

THE INADVERTENT REVOLUTION

Those in the White House and in Congress who governed us in the 1940s and 1950s were deeply aware that the world was changing more radically than ever before. They devoted most of their efforts to dealing with the changing world outside our borders. It took them many years to realize that the country changing the most rapidly was neither a Communist nation nor one of the new emergent nations of Asia or Africa. It was the U.S.A.

America's population had begun growing at a rate hitherto typical only of peasant nations. The nation accumulated wealth faster than any nation ever had. Technology advanced at an unheard-of rate, and machines and computers increasingly did work formerly done only by human beings.

Washington's neglect of our changing nation led to troubles. In the richest country in the world, at least thirty million Americans were left behind in poverty. In cities, crime began increasing several times as fast as the population. Lakes and rivers, one after another, were no longer able to sustain fish life due to pollution caused by our increasing population. Pollution of the air from multiplying factories and automobiles grew at such a rate that experts predicted the continent would be unable to sustain human life within a hundred years.

Through most of our history, the two "active" branches of our government in Washington—the Executive and the Legislative—have normally taken the initiative and met our national problems. But in this period of neglect, the usually passive third branch began to act. In the mid-fifties the Supreme Court launched its most creative period since John Marshall.

THE WARREN COURT

In September, 1953, President Eisenhower made an appointment which by itself would have made his terms memorable. He appointed Earl Warren, the Governor of California, to be Chief Justice of the United States.

Warren, whose family name was originally Varran, was the son of a Norwegian father and a Swedish mother. He was a big polar bear of a man, white-thatched, pleasant in manner but firm in action. He shared Eisenhower's gift of popularity. He had been elected Governor of the fastest growing state three times, the last time as the candidate of both Republican and Democratic parties.

The big Californian arrived on the high court to find the government marking time in a nation starved for attention. Two problems in particular called for immediate action.

First, by the middle of the twentieth century seventy percent of Americans had gathered in one percent of our area—the cities. Yet political power remained where it had been in the nineteenth century—in the countryside. One example—not as bad as many others —was Atlanta, Georgia. It had 500,000 inhabitants but was allowed to elect only one senator to the state legislature. A nearby rural community with only 16,000 inhabitants also elected one senator. In effect, each rural citizen had thirty times the vote of each citizen who lived in Atlanta. The cities had big problems of worsening traffic congestion, slums, crime, and water and air pollution. And cities paid the most taxes to state and federal governments. Yet, they could get little of the help they needed from these governments because politicians pay more attention to areas with greater voting power.

The second problem was different but related. Of all the people who left the countryside to live in cities, those in greatest distress were Negro Americans. They were made vividly aware of their condition by the spread of television, which told them in hundreds of commercials a day what a rich nation they lived in—one in which they had little share. The sensitivity of Negroes about "second-class" citizenship was made greater by the desegregation of the armed forces under Truman and then Eisenhower in the Korean War. Men who risk life equally cannot placidly return to a civilian life in which they may do nothing else equally.

But above all, by now a considerable number of young Negroes were making their way through college and becoming articulate professional men and women. Negro ministers and Negro lawyers noted that the laws of both God and man, if enforced, were on the

Chief Justice Earl Warren

side of equal rights. They began to insist on enforcement. They turned to the courts.

The Warren Court, as the Supreme Court came to be called at this time, agreed to hear the famous case of *Brown v. Board of Education.* In this case Negro lawyers sought to prove that separate schools for whites and Negroes meant in fact inferior schools for Negroes.

On May 17, 1954, a unanimous Court handed down its decision. It stated that in our time a decent education is essential to the enjoyment of any of the rights guaranteed in the Constitution. "Separate educational facilities," the new Chief Justice said in his opinion, "are inherently unequal." In no real sense could Negroes receiving inferior education be said to be enjoying their constitutional rights. Segregated schooling was therefore unconstitutional, and schools must be desegregated "with all deliberate speed." That phrase was elastic: It could mean a week or five years. The rest of the language of this far-reaching ruling was flat and undramatic—the price Warren is thought to have paid in order to prevent three of the nine justices from dissenting. He wanted the ruling unanimous to add to its authority.

The effects of this great decision were tremendous and are continuing. Every September for several years there was at last one school crisis as all-white schools resisted the entrance of Negro students. Twice federal troops had to be called out to maintain order. But increasingly, in the middle sixties, resistance to the ruling dwindled.

The Supreme Court ruling started a "rights revolution." The year after the ruling, 1955, the Reverend Martin Luther King led a successful boycott of segregated city buses in Montgomery, Alabama. In 1960 began the first lunch counter sit-ins by Negroes to break segregation of those facilities. In 1961 began the first freedom rides to desegregate transportation accommodations in the nation.

In 1963, the civil rights movement undertook a great "March on Washington." Negroes and whites gathered in hundreds of thousands before the Lincoln Memorial. There Marian Anderson sang as she had in 1939; and Martin Luther King and others made speeches. They demanded action by Congress to secure rights, and —as we shall see—they got it. The whole complex structure of discrimination began to creak and to fracture.

Meanwhile, the Warren Court had moved into a host of fields— regulating television commercials, defining Congress's powers of investigation (which had repeatedly been overstepped in the

McCarthy era), assuring legal help to poor defendants, and many others.

The ruling Warren was by far proudest of was none of these; nor was it the great school decision of 1954. It was his opinion in the case of *Reynolds v. Sims* (1964), which in fact was six cases rolled into one. Here Warren declared that the meaning and purpose of democracy was frustrated by our badly apportioned state legislatures. "Citizens, not history or economic interests, cast votes. . . . Legislators represent people, not trees or acres." In the same year, the Court ruled that the House of Representatives in Washington was also malapportioned and gave rural interests a power their numbers in no way justified.

These decisions were followed by reapportionments of legislatures all over the nation, adjusting America to its own changed situation. The idea even caught fire abroad: In Rhodesia, black citizens demonstrated in the streets chanting, "One man one vote," a slogan inspired by the decisions of the U.S. Supreme Court.

Big changes, however necessary, are never welcomed by everyone. All over the nation reactionary groups erected great billboards

Crowds massed around the Lincoln Memorial during the "March on Washington."

Khrushchev measured his new, youthful adversary. He had met Kennedy briefly in 1959 on his tour of America, when the young man was a member of the Senate Foreign Relations Committee. In April, 1961, when Kennedy had been President three months, Khrushchev watched from his distance an American-sponsored invasion of Cuba. It was a failure, the worst blunder in the modern history of American foreign affairs. It is not surprising that Khrushchev decided that the young man was a handsome ornament but not much of an opponent.

The new President felt it was urgent that he and Khrushchev meet and understand one another. He proposed a meeting, which took place in Vienna in June, 1961, when Kennedy had been President five months. The Russian was deaf to proposals to lower tensions. And he repeated a threat to force the Western nations out of West Berlin—to remove, as he put it, "this splinter from the heart of Europe." The President felt it best to be explicit: The United States would resist any such attempt with force. Khrushchev said he would meet force with force. Kennedy said, "Mister Chairman, it is going to be a cold winter."

Khrushchev proceeded to take menacing actions in Berlin and elsewhere. The greatest of his many threats took place in Communist Cuba, ninety miles from the United States. In 1962, Russia began sending Cuba great quantities of Russian weapons and many Russian troops and trainers. The President grew deeply worried. He authorized U-2 reconnaissance planes to survey Cuba. These planes could take photographs from ten miles up that could show an object as small as a golf ball on the ground.

On October 16, 1962, the President was given U-2 photographs showing that Soviet nuclear missiles were being planted in Cuba— forty-two of them, able to travel in seconds from 1,100 to 2,200 miles and hit almost any American city. Each could do the damage of twenty to thirty of the Hiroshima bombs.

We shall probably never know exactly what Khrushchev had in mind, but this is a guess made in the White House: When the missiles were ready, Khrushchev would reveal their existence and demand that we get out of Berlin. America would break up in a great debate about what to do. The Allies would bicker and the U.N. would consult endlessly. Finally, the United States would agree to get out of Berlin rather than face the horrors of a war. The people of West Berlin, who had three times voted more than ninety-seven percent against the Communists, would be handed over to them. No nation would trust America after that. The brief period of

Within the image:
- 5 TRUCKS UNDER CAMOUFLAGE NETTING
- CABLE
- MISSILE ERECTOR
- THEODOLITE STATION
- 5 TRUCKS UNDER CAMOUFLAGE NETTIN[G]
- MISSILE SHELTER TENTS

American power that began in peacetime under Truman would be over.

For six days after the missiles had been spotted, Kennedy kept to his normal schedule of appointments to avoid giving an impression that anything was amiss. But lights blazed through the night in the White House and the Pentagon and the State Department as plans were laid. Twice in those six days, former President Eisenhower was brought by helicopter to the White House for briefing. Once the President phoned all three ex-Presidents—Hoover, Truman, and Eisenhower—to explain his plans. All supported him. At 7:00 P.M. on Monday, October 22, the President spoke from the White House to the nation and the world on radio and television. He said:

"Within the past week, unmistakable evidence has established the fact that a series of offensive missile sites is now in preparation on [Cuba]. . . . Each of these missiles is capable of striking Washing-

One of many reconnaissance photographs proving the establishment of missile bases in Cuba.

*President Kennedy as he
spoke from the White House
to the nation
and to the world,
October 22, 1962.*

ton, D. C., the Panama Canal, Cape Canaveral, Mexico City, or any other city in the southeastern part of the United States, Central America, or the Caribbean area."

He announced that he was ordering the U.S. Navy to "quarantine" Cuba to prevent further missiles or parts from arriving. He called on Khrushchev to remove those that were already there. Then he spoke the words a generation had feared to hear from one of the giant powers: "It shall be the policy of this nation to regard any nuclear missile launched from Cuba against any nation in the Western Hemisphere as an attack by the Soviet Union on the United States requiring full retaliatory response upon the Soviet Union."

The world was shocked. But none of the consequences Khrushchev presumably intended in fact occurred. The Latin American nations stood as one by the President. So did the European Allies. So did the American people.

There were some confused communications from Khrushchev, one saying America was guilty of "piracy." But Kennedy moved ahead. The biggest invasion force since World War II was mounted in Florida, ready to move into Cuba. Twenty-six American warships moved out to block the accesses to Cuba, with 150 more in reserve in case Russian warships moved in. Within hours of having to face the American ships, some sixteen Russian cargo vessels on the way to Cuba received orders to turn back. American planes shadowed them all the way back to Soviet ports. One of Khrushchev's communications to Kennedy indicated personal panic. Finally on Sunday morning, October 28, Khrushchev announced that he would withdraw the missiles from Cuba under inspection.

Later that morning in the Cabinet room of the White House, according to the President's aide, Theodore Sorenson, "John F. Kennedy entered and we all stood up. He had, as Harold Macmillan would later say, earned his place in history by this one act alone. He had been engaged in a personal as well as national contest for world leadership and he had won. . . . he looked 'ten feet tall.'"

The opinion was widely expressed that this was the climax of the long Cold War with Russia. Many problems came unstuck after this. The Russian threat to Berlin was abandoned. The nuclear powers signed an agreement to explode no more bombs in the atmosphere. There was a marked liberalization of life in Russia and in the Russian satellite nations. Americans congratulated themselves on all these successes, but President Kennedy warned them against the danger of believing that this was the end of friction with Russia.

As messages between Kennedy and Khrushchev in the crisis had taken a long time in transmission—one took 18 hours at a time when minutes counted—it was agreed to open up a "hot line" between the Kremlin in Moscow and the Pentagon in Washington. The teletype line provides direct immediate contact between the two places 24 hours a day. At the Washington end, the line is tied into the President's communications system wherever he may move. At given times each day Russia sends us practice messages consisting of passages from Russian literary classics, and we send them messages made up of quotations from famous American authors. If the line is ever interrupted, as it was once cut by the plow of a farmer in Finland, a backup line through other countries is automatically activated so that there is never a break in communication.

It is difficult to recapture the tension of a crisis successfully overcome. Perhaps the best way to sense something of its pressure is to know the awesome responsibility Kennedy carried and to imagine his fears as he sat in his oval office looking out on the darkened lawn of the White House, waiting for Khrushchev's response. He had at his command a quantity of power that no other person had ever possessed since time began. It worked out at 30,000 pounds of TNT explosive for every human being alive.

John Kennedy was a voracious reader with a strongly developed sense of history. His wife had the rare gift of good taste. These two qualities combined to make the Kennedy years among the most hopeful ever for the federal city.

Mrs. Kennedy enlisted the interest of the nation by redecorating the White House with furniture from its great periods. She then took part in an extremely popular television program, in which she directed a tour of the most famous residence in the land.

Kennedy appointed an adviser on Washington affairs to his White House staff. Also, he appointed the first Negro to the three-man Board of Commissioners who run the city on Congress's orders. He had a new code drawn up for the design of public buildings. It said, in a phrase that would have mightily pleased Pierre L'Enfant, "The design for public buildings must come from the architects to the government and not vice versa." He also gave his blessing to a design for the whole metropolitan Washington area, called the Year 2000 Plan.

The first result was a new design for Lafayette Square, facing the White House. In 1958, a plan was drawn up to demolish all the historic buildings on the famous old square, including Decatur House and Dolly Madison's home, and to replace them with huge, dull government office buildings. Kennedy canceled the plan and had an architect draw up another: The small historic buildings would be preserved or restored; the government office buildings would be erected behind them in a style in keeping with the appearance and atmosphere of the old square.

L'Enfant had hoped to make the nation's premier boulevard,

Dulles International Airport, serving Washington, D.C.

Pennsylvania Avenue, a ceremonial way of beauty and distinction. But his hope had never been realized. Now Kennedy put a committee to work; it drew up a plan to rebuild much of the avenue, leaving broad plazas before some public buildings, raising sidewalks, and planting triple rows of trees on each side of the street. The Capitol Hill end of the avenue would have a reflecting pool; the White House end would be turned into the biggest public square in the nation, National Square, to compare with the Place de la Concorde in Paris.

One vast improvement, planned under Truman and advanced under Eisenhower, began to take shape under Kennedy: the rebuilding of the whole southwest quarter of Washington. This area, neighboring the wharves where Civil War supplies were once unloaded, was the worst slum in the city. Eighty percent of the inhabitants were Negroes. Half the houses had no plumbing. All but a few historic homes were now demolished and 550 acres were cleared. Then new houses and buildings in a variety of styles arose, among them Washington's own city theater, the Arena Stage. The project seemed expensive. But in fact it returned eight times as much tax money as the area had yielded before, and became a genuinely racially integrated section of the city.

The number of unhandsome new buildings (the new Rayburn Office Building, for instance, and the new State Department quarters neighboring those of the 1940s in Foggy Bottom) still exceeded the number of fine new ones (such as Dulles International Airport, designed by Eero Saarinen). But at least people had been made conscious of the need for a change.

Robert Weaver, federal housing chief (later first Secretary of Housing and Urban Development) at the site of a housing project in southwest Washington.

THE SLASHED FABRIC

The art of self-government is the most difficult of man's endeavors. Very few peoples have acquired even a partial mastery of it. Of all the processes of self-government, the hardest to master by far is transition—the orderly transfer of power from one group to another. With all their imperfections, the generations who came to Washington to practice the art built their government well and amended it with more practical wisdom than might normally be expected from ordinary humans. An example of how well they had worked occurred late in November of 1963.

Young John Kennedy, riding in an open car in Dallas, Texas, was shot to death by a madman. The fabric of government was violently slashed. It was one of the most stunning individual tragedies of the

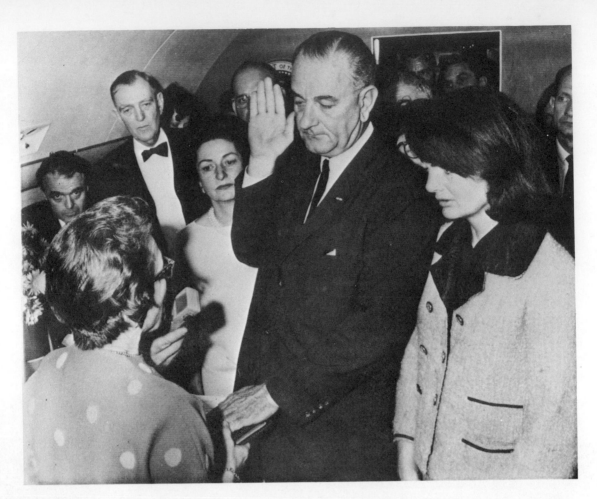

*Lyndon B. Johnson
is sworn in as 36th President
in the Presidential jet plane.
His wife is at left,
Mrs. Kennedy at right.*

present century. Television carried the news and the succeeding events into every American home, and Telstar carried them into homes overseas.

People in London went to Grosvenor Square in hundreds to stand silently before the American Embassy, just because they felt they should do something. A Japanese farmer walked eighteen miles into Tokyo to stand with his head bowed before the American Embassy there. In Berlin, people darkened their homes and put lighted candles in their windows.

Nowhere was sorrow deeper than in the federal city which had found, and now suddenly lost, a champion for its problems. Yet immediately, the slashed ends of the fabric of government in Washington knitted back together again.

It sounded feelingless—but it was not—that the Government Accounting Office completed the records of a federal official listed as "John F. Kennedy, President," by paying up his salary for fourteen twenty-fourths of November 22, 1963. He had been declared dead in a Dallas hospital at 2:00 P.M., or 1400 hours. A federal official listed as "Lyndon B. Johnson, President" started his salary at that same hour.

The only change as prompt as that was the shift of the "walking courier." He is the conspicuous officer—who tries not to be conspicuous—who carries in a case the constantly updated instructions for the President to follow in ordering a nuclear attack. He is under orders never to let more than one door separate him from the Chief Executive. When Kennedy was declared dead, he moved from a chair outside the Dallas hospital room where the late President's body rested to a chair outside the hospital room where the new President waited.

Within minutes of the shooting, the White House staff asked all nine of America's combat commands over the globe to be alert and ready. By the time the great Presidential jet plane, bearing the bronze coffin, landed at Andrews Air Force Base near Washington late that afternoon, the new President in the same plane had already taken up controls of the office by radio communication with aides.

While the coffin lay in the East Room of the White House, on the same catafalque that had borne Lincoln's body, seven scholars worked through the night in the Library of Congress studying the

President Kennedy's coffin in the East Room, resting on the same catafalque as President Lincoln's (page 66).

174

records of Lincoln's funeral in order to plan Kennedy's. When the coffin was moved up Pennsylvania Avenue to lie in state in the rotunda of the Capitol, television cameras outside the White House picked up the poignant sight of the late President's ship models and other office decorations being carried out to ready the office for the new President.

By the day of the funeral, when great world leaders followed the coffin on foot up Connecticut Avenue to St. Matthew's Cathedral, the new President was as much in control as if he had always been President. The actual process of government had not even quivered in the tragic, abrupt transition.

Earlier in the year, President Kennedy had crossed the Potomac and gone to Arlington Cemetery for a ceremony. On his way back he paused a short way down the hill from Robert E. Lee's house and the tomb of Pierre L'Enfant. He told his companion, Secretary of Defense McNamara, that he liked the view from there better than any he knew, and he added, "I could stay here forever."

He will. Now, when the trees are bare in winter, and you drive along the Potomac at night, you may see the floodlighted Lee mansion at the top of the hill, and a little below it a single pinpoint of flame flickering like a distant star. The flame is meant to burn eternally. Beneath it lies John Kennedy, who was President of the United States for a little less than three years.

Many foreign dignitaries flew to Washington for President Kennedy's funeral. Front row, from left: President Heinrich Luebke of West Germany; President Charles de Gaulle of France; Queen Frederika of Greece; King Baudouin of Belgium; Emperor Haile Selassie of Ethiopia; President Diosdado Macapagal of the Philippine Republic.

THE MASTER OF CAPITOL HILL

President Kennedy's grave

President Kennedy became first in the hearts of the American people and first in the respect of world leaders. But he never won Congress to his side. In his first year, he proposed a comprehensive program of action to meet the growing problems of our swelling urban population, and Congress passed some of it. In his second year, he proposed as much, but Congress passed less. In his third year, Congress refused to act at all, and legislation stagnated completely.

Because of Congress's hostility, Kennedy had sought to advance civil rights by concentrating on executive actions that needed no Congressional approval. But in 1963, outbreaks of violence in cities north and south made it urgent that Congress take new, vigorous action. The President introduced a far-reaching bill which, among other provisions, would make it a federal offense for restaurants and hotels to refuse Negroes accommodations. The prospects of the bill's passage seemed very poor indeed.

The main cause of Kennedy's failure was an unlikely combination of forces in Congress. The Southern Democrats, who were sometimes fairly progressive in respect to social measures, bitterly opposed civil-rights legislation. The Northern conservatives, who were fairly progressive in respect to civil rights, bitterly opposed having the government take on more projects and spend more money. The two found that when they supported one another they could stop any legislation. So they formed a "coalition" and made Congress a means of blocking laws rather than passing laws.

A problem often produces a man to meet it. This intolerable condition of Congressional stagnation did just that. It is doubtful if Washington has ever known a figure who was so wholly the master of the legislative process as the man who now became the thirty-sixth President of the United States.

Lyndon Baines Johnson had been born to the poverty of the over-grazed and over-farmed Texas hill country. He was a gangling string-bean boy, who grew to be an inch taller than John Kennedy, an inch shorter than Washington and Lincoln. His mother was a schoolteacher and his father a politician. He tried both professions, plus a little hobo-ing.

In the black, aching pit of the Depression in 1932, he went to Washington to be secretary to a Congressman. He found that Congress was a clearing house where shrewd men traded in power, and he decided that was the life for him. He became a Congressman, then a Senator, then the youngest Senate leader the Democrats had ever had. He rapidly developed a reputation for skill at getting things done in Congress, a skill that approached genius.

His most conspicuous surface feature was a manner and an accent usually identified with hillbilly politicians. It was unfortunate because it caused many people to underestimate the man of great substance and deep dedication within. His chief political asset was an inner drive to get things done that was about as easy to withstand as an alpine landslide.

Eight Vice Presidents have succeeded to the White House on the deaths of Presidents. Of them all, Johnson had least time left before having to run for reelection—only eleven months. He used the time, his gifted wife said, as if "there was never going to be a tomorrow."

His job, said Kennedy's Press Chief, Pierre Salinger, "was about like taking over the driver's seat of a bus that had run up against a brick wall." All legislation was stalled, and the passage of the Civil Rights Bill had become crucial. The Republican Senate leader said he could not vote for it. The Democratic Senate leader said he could not mobilize enough votes to stop Southerners from filibustering it to death.

Four days after Kennedy's burial Johnson addressed Congress and zeroed in on the essential problem. "Our most immediate tasks," he said, "are here on this Hill." He returned to the White House and his telephone console and began to pull the "coalition" of Southern

Lyndon B. Johnson at the telephone

Democrats and Northern conservatives apart. His basic method, it is said, was to learn what every member of Congress wanted most and what every member feared most—and then to translate that knowledge into votes.

His general policy was to woo the Northern conservatives by taking the Kennedy budget to pieces and putting it back together in a month at a much lower figure. He was not only thrifty but he made sure to *appear* thrifty. He began turning off the White House lights until tourists' complaints filled the papers. He pointed out that he was saving the people money. He began slashing outdated defense installations till members of Congress complained. In the end the Northern conservatives were no longer supporting the Southerners; they were supporting Johnson. Then a vote was held to break the Southern filibuster against the Rights Bill and, in an action that is historic, it succeeded. The most far-reaching Civil Rights Bill since the Emancipation Proclamation passed. Everything else came loose in Congress now, and legislation began to flow.

By this time, November, 1964, Johnson was up for election. He sought to win everybody and almost did. The vote confirmed him in the Presidency by the biggest popular majority in American history. He swept in with him the most favorable and progressive Congress any President had ever had. For the first time anyone could recall, all three branches of the government were in political harmony.

The rulings of the Warren Court were beginning to loosen the rural grip on Congress and on state legislatures, weakening the strength of Northern conservatives. Johnson introduced a historic voting rights bill to secure Negroes the ballot in the South; this threatened to weaken the force of the old style Southern Democrats. Thus both parts of the "coalition" that had stalled Kennedy's program were losing ground.

Johnson's first Congress after the election—his first in his own right, in 1965—was a veritable whirlwind of action. It passed more durable social legislation than any other, including Wilson's famous special sessions of 1913 and Roosevelt's first New Deal Congress in 1933.

After this early peak of success, Johnson faced pitfalls that almost every President has known. One was the fact that Congress nearly always recovers the jealous pride built into it by the Constitution and begins resisting even the cleverest Chief Executive. Another was the rude intrusion of foreign crisis: The Cold War seemed to transfer itself from the Western world, where it had been nearly mastered, to the Far East, where Communists now became aggressive. Finally Johnson faced the difficulties created by his own unique personality: restless, perfectionist, irritable when he could not win every contest—qualities which got action but which also aroused antagonisms. When his troubles seemed most oppressive, a reporter asked him if they were not too much for him to bear. He shook his head and summed up the story of his office in a single phrase: "That's what Presidents are for."

It is hard to guess how future historians may list Kennedy and Johnson on the scale of greatness, for the recent Presidents are too close to us. However, by the end of Lyndon Johnson's first thousand days in office, few observers would begrudge him the judgment that he was certainly one of the most effective Presidents ever in getting things done.

Few Presidents have felt a greater need for a wife's help or received so much of it. Mrs. Johnson in the White House planned a vigorous campaign for beautification of a nation which had grown too rich and too mechanized too quickly. Her special interest was the city of Washington. In the tradition of Mrs. Kennedy, she took

Mrs. Johnson at the planting of a 20-foot red oak in downtown Washington. With her is John Duncan, member of the city's three-man Board of Commissioners.

part in a popular television program telling the story of the city and urging its improvement. The Johnsons' strong concern for the capital city of the nation was the source of one of the President's few political setbacks.

THE LAST COLONY

Lyndon Johnson's winning streak in Congress was interrupted on September 29, 1965. For three days, the House of Representatives had been debating a bill to bring the American Revolution to Washington and let the city elect its own city government. The debate began with a Congressman asking that visitors' galleries be cleared lest passions over the issue lead to trouble. It ended with defeat for the home rule bill and for the President who had proposed it.

The debate brought together the essential facts about our nation's capital and why it is the kind of place it is. As we have seen, until the 1870s Washington elected its own city government, just as other cities did. Then Congress withdrew the right. One reason it gave was that people who were unable to stop Alexander Shepherd from

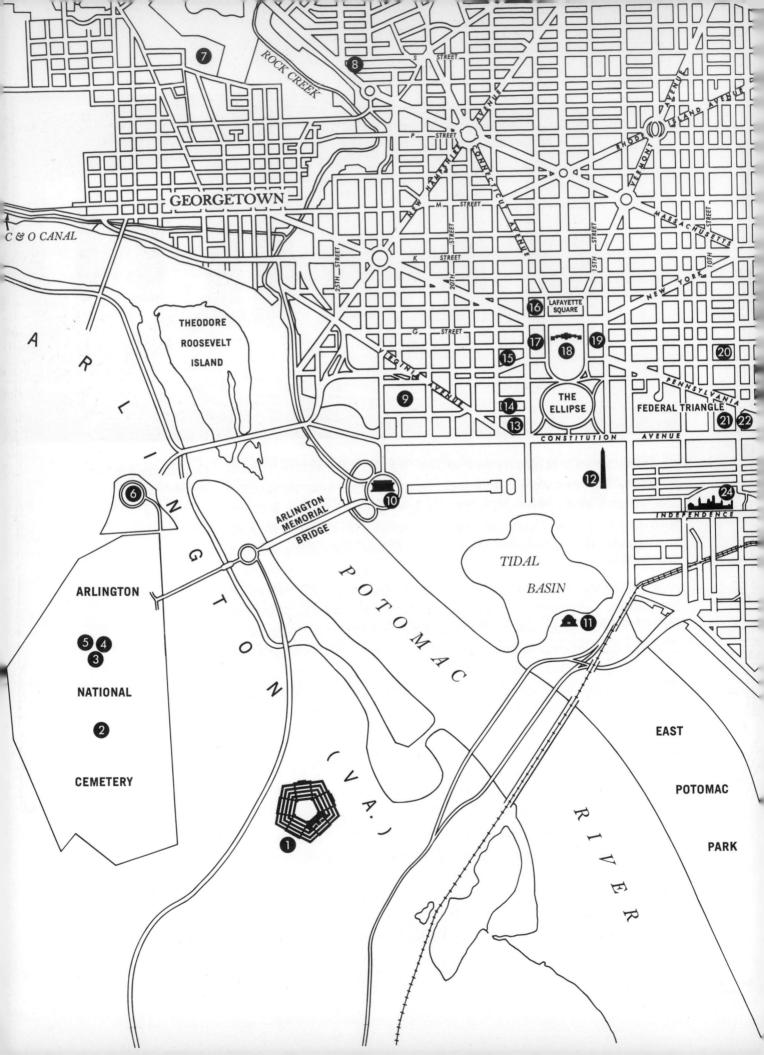

ROCK CREEK

7

8

S STREET

GEORGETOWN

P STREET

M STREET

C & O CANAL

NEW HAMPSHIRE AVENUE

CONNECTICUT AVENUE

K STREET

RHODE ISLAND AVENUE

VERMONT AVENUE

MASSACHUSETTS

NEW YORK AVENUE

A R L I N G T O N

THEODORE
ROOSEVELT
ISLAND

25TH STREET

20TH STREET

G STREET

LAFAYETTE
SQUARE

16

17   18   19

20

15TH STREET

10TH STREET

VIRGINIA AVENUE

9

15

14

THE
ELLIPSE

PENNSYLVANIA

FEDERAL TRIANGLE

21   22

13

CONSTITUTION   AVENUE

12

6

ARLINGTON

ARLINGTON MEMORIAL
BRIDGE

10

P O T O M A C

TIDAL
BASIN

24

INDEPENDENCE

5   4

3

NATIONAL

2

11

CEMETERY

(V A .)

R I V E R

EAST

POTOMAC

PARK

1

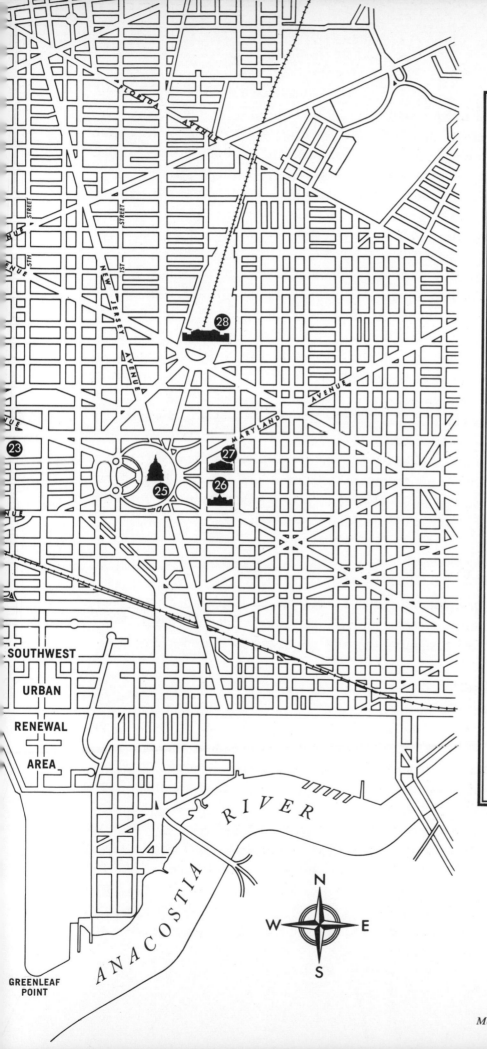

ARCHIVES BUILDING (22)

ARLINGTON HOUSE (5)

BLAIR HOUSE (16)

THE CAPITOL (25)

CONSTITUTION HALL (14)

DEPARTMENT OF JUSTICE (FBI) (21)

DEPARTMENT OF STATE (9)

DUMBARTON OAKS (7)

EXECUTIVE OFFICE BUILDING (17)

FORD'S THEATER (20)

JEFFERSON MEMORIAL (11)

KENNEDY GRAVE (4)

L'ENFANT'S TOMB (3)

LIBRARY OF CONGRESS (26)

LINCOLN MEMORIAL (10)

MARINE WAR MEMORIAL (6)

NATIONAL GALLERY OF ART (23)

OCTAGON HOUSE (15)

PAN AMERICAN UNION (13)

THE PENTAGON (1)

SMITHSONIAN INSTITUTION (24)

SUPREME COURT (27)

TOMB OF THE UNKNOWN SOLDIER (2)

TREASURY BUILDING (19)

UNION STATION (28)

WASHINGTON MONUMENT (12)

WHITE HOUSE (18)

WILSON HOUSE (8)

Map based on map © General Drafting Co., Inc.

Washington issues. This fact the small-town politicians exploited fully in the debate.

They said, correctly, that Washington receives more federal money than any other city—but neglected to point out that since it is deprived of normal sources of income, it could not function at all without federal money. The Negro poor were depicted as living a life of splendid ease on welfare moneys. It was not pointed out that even with federal help, twenty-five percent of the population of the city lived below subsistence level.

Frightening visions were painted of an irresponsible city government doing such things as erecting commercial billboards on the Capitol lawn—though the home rule bill clearly left the control of federal property wholly to the federal, not the city, government.

A three-day barrage of arguments like these injected doubts in the minds of tired Congressmen. In the end the House voted to accept a delayed home rule program. This put the issue back in the hands of the House District committee, where a tiny minority could once more prevent any action.

But at least the debate won wider attention for the city's predicament. And larger trends in the nation—in favor of helping our neglected cities—were moving with such momentum that, for once, a spirit of hopelessness did not follow defeat.

A STORY FOR OTHERS TO FINISH

Washington entered the last third of the twentieth century with more than its share of the problems sorely afflicting cities. But it also had more than its share of promises that the problems would be met.

The great challenges of the capital attracted an unusual number of people with qualifications to face them. By the rough measurement of college training, Washington had the best educated population in the nation: Fifteen percent of the metropolitan area's population had received four years of college education. San Francisco and Oakland together were not even a close second with ten percent.

From the time of Thomas Jefferson, the city had a reputation for being culturally provincial. Now it had its own theater, its own ballet, its own symphony—all young but full of hope. It had five universities available to it, though like other Washington facilities none had enough resources to rank among the first-rate schools.

In Washington began the modern trend of Negroes moving into

centers of cities and whites moving out of them to the suburbs. But here as nowhere else, contact between the races was maintained, and what sociologists call "a dialogue" persisted. An organization, Neighbors, Inc., was busy trying to integrate neighborhoods. Opportunity for the capable and the resolute was kept open in the city—the birthplace of Robert C. Weaver, who in 1965 became the first Negro in the President's cabinet, and of Senator Edward W. Brooke of Massachusetts, who in 1966 won the highest elective office held by a Negro since Reconstruction.

The city had a status to live up to. It had become beyond challenge the leading capital of Western civilization—the way of life

For each resident of Washington, there are twelve visitors every year.

begun in ancient Athens and passed down the ages through Rome and the great capitals of Western Europe.

Inside America, no organization or industry of importance had by the middle sixties failed to move its headquarters to Washington. Long since, for example, the headquarters of the machine tool industry—an industry basic to an industrial society—had left Cleveland where tools are made and moved to Washington where decisions are made.

Outside America, no one was surprised when Belgium sought to explain its troubles in the Congo by holding a press conference—not in Brussels but in Washington. No one disputed the judgment of a great London newspaper that published a photo of a newly elected American president with the caption, "Leader of the West."

More journalists and more diplomats gathered in and passed on information from Washington than any other city in the world. More than ten million tourists visited the place each year. That is a larger ratio of visitors to inhabitants—12 to 1—than even the great tourist centers in Europe know.

The city, whose chief industry is the manufacture of great decisions, faces a host of missions it does not want but cannot evade. By far its most important mission is to keep peace in a world grown both more dangerous and more difficult to cope with. The great capitals of the past, from ancient Rome onward, kept order by methods of imperialism. Washington is the first world capital to try to keep order by opposite methods. Wherever its emissaries have moved they have sought—as in post-World War II Germany and Japan—to bring about government by the free choice of the inhabitants rather than by imperial dictate from Washington. Imperialism has always meant exploitation; but Washington's policy has been to *give* to the people of troubled nations rather than take away. This is the opposite of exploitation.

Against the long measuring stick of history, the period of Washington's ascendancy in the world has been very brief. In so short a time it is impossible to predict whether the city will carry out its huge, unsought tasks with success. One can only feel sure that the story is not over and that, indeed, it has not even approached its climax.

The success of the venture launched by George Washington and Thomas Jefferson and Pierre L'Enfant clearly depends on the courage and wisdom of some future generation. Very possibly it might be the generation for whom this book was written.

THE
DECLARATION OF INDEPENDENCE
THE
CONSTITUTION
OF THE
UNITED STATES OF AMERICA
AND THE
BILL OF RIGHTS

INDEX

Abolitionists, 43
Acheson, Dean, 144–45
Adams, Abigail, 20, 40
Adams, Henry, 71
Adams, John, 20, 22–23, 25, 27
Adams, John Quincy, 34, 37, 40, 77
Adams, Mrs. John Quincy, 34
Adenauer, Konrad, 165
Agricultural Adjustment Act (AAA), 110, 115
Alcott, Louisa May, 54
Alexandria, Va., 3–4, 19, 48–49
American Federation of Labor (A.F.L.), 119–20
American Institute of Architects, 31, 32
American Revolution, 5, 7–8, 127
Anacostia River, 3, 183
Analostan Island, 62
Anderson, Marian, 122–23, 162
Andrews Air Force Base, 156, 173
Antietam, Battle of, 58
Architectural Forum, 158
Archives Building, 97, 183, 187
Arena Stage, 171
Arlington Cemetery, 52, 174, 182
Arlington Heights, 18, 49
Arlington House, 50, 97, 183
Arlington Memorial Bridge, 97, 182
Army of Northern Virginia, 55
Army of the Potomac, 55, 57–58
Arnold, Samuel, 65
Atlantic Charter, 134
Atomic bomb, 139, 151
Atzerodt, George A., 65
Axis powers, 123, 128

Baltimore, Md., 37
Baltimore and Ohio Railroad, 37
Banneker, Benjamin, 12, 43
Barton, Clara, 54
Baruch, Bernard, 87, 143

Baruch Plan, for nuclear weapons, 142
"Battle Hymn of the Republic," 54
Bell, Alexander Graham, 77
Berlin, West, Soviet threat to, 166, 169
Black Codes, 61, 70
"Bladensburg Races," 29–30
Blair, Francis P., 35, 51
Blair House, 35, 51, 149, 183
Blue Eagle, 117
Bonus Marchers (1932), 104–07
Booth, John Wilkes, 54, 63–65
Borah, William E., 91, 125
Braddock's Rock, in Potomac, 22
Brady, Mathew, 47, 50, 59, 64
Brooke, Edward W., 185
Brown, John, 45, 50
Brown v. Board of Education, 162
Brownlow, Louis, 99
Buchanan, James, 45
Bull Run, First Battle of, 55–56
Bull Run, Second Battle of, 58
Burnes, Davey, 14, 19, 82
Burr, Aaron, 23
Byrnes, James, 135

Calhoun, John C., 134
Capitol building, 13, 27, 44, 50, 52–53, 102, 105, 183
 burned by British, 30
 design of, 21–22
 dome of, 21–22, 45, 53
 rotunda of, 18, 40–41, 53, 66, 75
 See also Congress House
Capitol Hill, 13, 19–20, 33, 83–84
Capone, Alphonse, 94, 95
Carroll, Daniel, of Carrollton, 15
Carroll, Daniel, of Duddington, 15–16, 18
Chamberlain, Neville, 124–25
Cherry Blossom Festival, 131
Chesapeake and Ohio Canal, 36–37, 112, 182
Chevy Chase farm, 76

Chicago Tribune, 148
Chicago World's Fair, 81
China, Communist, 151
"Church of the Presidents," 35
Churchill, Winston, 86–87, 126–28, 134, 139
Civil-rights legislation, 175–77
Civil War, 26, 33, 43, 48–61, 67, 86, 102, 129
Civilian Conservation Corps (CCC), 110
Cleveland, Frances, 76
Cleveland, Grover, 76
Cleveland, Rose, 76
Cleveland Heights, 76
Cold War, 143–45, 151–52, 169, 178
Collins, Ross, 122
Commager, Henry Steele, 32
Community Chest, 99, 131
Compromise of 1850, 44
Congress, U.S., 33–34, 40–41, 81
 and civil-rights legislation, 175–77
 and Johnson, Andrew, 68–71
 and Johnson, Lyndon B., 176–78
 neutrality laws passed by (1935–1937), 124
 and self-rule for Washington, 73, 75–76, 179–81, 184
 seniority in, 82
 wealthy members of, 76
 See also House of Representatives; Senate
Congress House (Capitol), 9, 11, 13, 20
Congress of Industrial Organizations (C.I.O.), 120
Connecticut Avenue, 174
Constitution, U.S., 23, 27, 94, 97, 116, 153, 178
 as flexible document, 28
 Madison as father of, 29
Constitution Avenue, 12, 14, 74, 136, 182
Constitution Hall, 122, 153, 183
Containment policy, toward Communism, 145, 155

Cooley, Harold O., 129
Coolidge, Calvin, 101, 119
Coolidge, Mrs. Calvin, 95
Cox, James M., 109
Cruikshank, Robert, 39
Cuba, 166–69
Custis-Lee Mansion, 50
Czechoslovakia, 146

Daughters of the American Revolution, 43, 114, 122–23, 153
Davis, Jefferson, 45
Decatur, Stephen, 34–35
Decatur House, 35, 170
Declaration of Independence, 97, 187
Delinquency, juvenile, 122
Democracy in America (Tocqueville), 141
Depression, Great, 102–04, 109, 121, 176
Dewey, Thomas E., 148
Dickens, Charles, 34
Digges, William D., 18
District of Columbia, 12, 43–44, 55, 91. *See also* Washington, D.C.
Dixiecrat party, 148
Donelson, Emily, 43
Drayton, Daniel, 44
Dulles, John Foster, 155–56
Dulles International Airport, 170, 171
Dumbarton Oaks, 134, 183
Duncan, John, 179

Early, Jubal, 60
East Potomac Park, 76, 182
Eighteenth Amendment, 94–95
Einstein, Albert, 138
Eisenhower, Dwight D.
  as army officer, 106, 132–33, 155
  as ex-President, 164, 167
  as NATO commander, 146, 148, 154
  as President, 25, 155–57, 159, 161
Eisenhower, Mrs. Dwight D., 159
Ellicott, Andrew, 12, 17–18
Emancipation Proclamation, 61, 177
Erie Canal, 37, 112
Everett, Edward, 47, 49
Executive branch, of federal government, 27, 160

Executive Mansion (White House), 25

Fair, Senator, 76
Fair Deal (Truman's), 147
Fair Employment Practices Code, 131
Fall, Albert B., 100
Farley, James A., 115
Federal government, three branches of, 27, 68, 160
Federal Hall, New York City, 9
Federal Reserve Act, 83
Federal Triangle, 97, 111, 182
Federalist Papers, 29
Federalists, 23
Fine Arts Commission, 112
"Foggy Bottom," 52, 144, 171
Ford, John T., 54
Ford's Theater, 54, 64, 66–67, 183
Foreign Affairs magazine, 145
Foreign aid (Point Four), 146–47
Fort Donelson, 60
Fort Duquesne, 5
Fort Knox, 114
Fort Lincoln, 62
Fort McHenry, 30–31
Fort Stevens, 60, 108
Fort Sumter, 48
Fourteen Points (Wilson's), 88–89
Foxhall, Henry, 36
Franco, Francisco, 124
Frankfurter, Felix, 87
Fredericksburg, Va., 59
Freedom figure, on Capitol dome, 45
French, Daniel Chester, 67
Fuchs, Klaus, 151

Garfield, James A., 77
Garfield Park, 16
Garner, John N., 117, 118, 135
George Washington University, 111
Georgetown, 3, 5, 33, 36–37, 41, 112, 182
Germany, 84–89, 123–24, 128, 186
Gettysburg, Battle of, 59
Glassford, Pelham, 104, 106
Government, U.S., three branches of, 27, 68, 160
Government Accounting Office, 172

Grant, Ulysses S., 60, 64, 70, 93
  and capture of Richmond, 61
  elected President, 74
Great Depression, 102–04, 109, 121, 176
Great Lakes, 37
Green, William, 119
Green Hill, 18
Greenhow, Rose, 56
Greenleaf, John, 36–38, 66
Greenleaf Point, 29, 36, 66, 183
Greenough, Horace, 40–41
Griswold, Congressman, 20

Hamilton, Alexander, 5, 7–9
Hanna, Mark, 78
Hanson, Royce, 158
Harding, Warren Gamaliel, 92–93, 96, 99–100, 108, 109
Harper's Ferry, 45, 48–49
Harrison, William Henry, 63
Hayes, Rutherford B., 76
H-bomb, 111
Hearst, William Randolph, 76
Herold, David E., 65
Hiroshima, 139
Hiss, Alger, 151
Hitler, Adolf, 123, 127, 136, 138–39
Hoban, James, 25–26
Holmes, Oliver Wendell, 60–61, 108
Hoover, Herbert C., 87, 102, 104–05, 107, 119, 158, 167
Hopkins, Harry, 110
"Hot line," 169
Houdon, Jean, 7
House Committee for D.C. Affairs, 180–81, 184
House Judiciary Committee, 117
House of Representatives, U.S., 20, 22–23, 27, 180
  Jefferson elected by, 23
Howard University, 72
Howe, Julia Ward, 54
Hughes, Charles Evans, 116–18
Hull, Cordell, 125
Hungarian revolt, 156
"Hunger Marchers" (1931), 104

Ickes, Harold, 122–23
Irving, Washington, 34
Isolationism, in United States, 80, 133–34, 144
Italy, 123–24, 128, 146
Iwo Jima, 136–38
Iwo Jima Memorial, 137

Jackson, Andrew, 26, 33, 63, 71, 117, 141
  appearance of, 39
  Battle of New Orleans won by, 32
  elected President, 38–40
  statue of, 41
  Union upheld by, 40
Jackson, Rachel, 39
Japan, 123, 127–28, 139, 153, 186
Jefferson, Thomas, 5, 7–8, 12–13, 16, 21, 25–26, 108, 184
  elected President, 23–24
  and Louisiana Purchase, 28
  and Marshall, 27–28
Jefferson Memorial, 12, 76, 111–12, 183
Jenkins Heights, 13, 20, 24
John F. Kennedy cultural center, 19
Johnson, Andrew, 45, 69, 74, 83, 89
  on trial in Senate, 70–71
Johnson, Hiram W., 91
Johnson, Lyndon B., 164, 172, 178
  relationship with Congress, 176–78, 181
Johnson, Mrs. Lyndon B., 178, 179
Judicial branch, of federal government, 27, 160
Jungk, Robert, 138

Kennan, George M., 145
Kennedy, John F., 25, 50, 66, 78, 158, 164–65, 170–71, 174–78
  and Khrushchev, 166, 168–69
  and missile crisis, 166–69
  murder of, 171–73
Kennedy, Mrs. John F., 164, 165, 172, 178
Kennedy cultural center, 19
Key, Francis Scott, 30, 42
Khrushchev, Nikita, 157, 165–66, 168–69

King, Martin Luther, 162
Kitty Hawk, 42, 96
Korean War, 131, 151–53, 161

Labor, organized, 93–94, 119–21
Lafayette, Marquis de, 127
Lafayette Square, 26, 35, 41, 170
LaFollette, Robert M., 85, 149
LaFollette, Robert M., Jr., 149–50, 158
Langley, Samuel P., 96
Latrobe, Benjamin, 22, 28, 35
League of Nations, 90–91, 134
Lear's Wharf, 19
Lee, Robert E., 45, 50–51, 58, 60–61, 63, 174
Leech, Margaret, quoted, 59
Legislative branch, of federal government, 27, 160
Lend-Lease Act, 127
L'Enfant, Pierre Charles, 2, 4–5, 7–9, 11, 16–19, 38
  letter to Washington, 9
  plan of, for Washington, D.C., 10–11, 13–14, 181
  streets designed by, 12–13, 33
  tomb of, 50, 174, 183
  tribute to, 18
Lewis, John L., 119–21
Library of Congress, 21–23, 77, 173, 183
Lincoln, Abraham, 25, 45, 51, 53–54, 57, 61, 63–64, 66, 68–69, 72
  criticisms of, 46–48
  elected President, 45–46
  and Grant, 59–60
  as greatest American, 46, 108
  murder of, 65, 69
Lincoln, Mrs. Abraham, 54
Lincoln Memorial, 12, 50, 66, 97, 112, 123, 183
Lindbergh, Charles, 97
Literary Digest, 115
Lodge, Henry Cabot, 90
Louisiana Purchase, 28

MacArthur, Douglas, 106–07, 132, 139, 152–54
McCarthy, Joseph R., 150–51, 164
McClellan, George B., 57–58
McCormick, Medill, 91

McKinley, William, 78–79, 83
McNamara, Robert S., 174
Madison, Dolly, 29, 35, 44, 170
Madison, James, 29, 31, 32
Mall, 13, 41–43, 81, 87, 97, 111, 132
Manhattan Project, 139
Marbury v. Madison, 28
March on Washington (1963), 162–63
Marshall, George, 133, 142, 144, 146, 155
Marshall, John, 27, 118, 160
Marshall Plan, 142, 145–46
Marx, Karl, 143
Mayflower Hotel, 119–20
Meade, George, 58
Mellon, Andrew, 111
Memorial Bridge, 97
Meridian Hill, 34
Merrimac, 58
Mills, Clark, 41
Mine Workers Union, 119
Monitor, 58
Monroe, James, 35
Monroney, Mike, 158
Monticello, 25
Moore, Charles, 17
Moore, Thomas, quoted, 33
Morgan, J. P., 79
Morison, Samuel E., 32
Mount Vernon, 4, 5, 19
Mussolini, Benito, 123

Napoleon, 28–29, 37–38, 139
National Archives, 97, 187
National Defense Research Council, 127
National Era, 44
National Gallery of Art, 111, 130, 183
National Industrial Recovery Act (NIRA), 110, 115
National Parks, 79
National Square, 171
Navy Yard, on Eastern Branch, 36
Nazism, 111
Negroes, 82, 98, 111, 121–22, 157, 161–62, 184–85
  aristocracy of, 43
  in armed forces, 62, 98–99, 131, 161
  desegregation of, 131, 162
  education of, 43, 72, 131, 161–62
  emancipation of, 61

employment of, 131
enslavement of, 43–45, 61
housing for, 171
opportunities for, 43, 131, 158, 185
voting by, 72, 76, 180
Neighbors, Inc., 181
New Deal (Roosevelt's), 110–12, 115, 119, 123, 178
New Frontier program (Kennedy's), 165
New Orleans, Battle of, 32
New York City, 5, 7, 9, 37, 72
New York Herald, 47, 49
New York State, 37
New York Times, 46, 83, 93, 103, 108, 145
Nixon, Richard, 164, 165, 193
Norris, George, 85
North Atlantic Treaty, 146
Northern Securities Corporation, 79
NRA, 117
Nuclear bomb, 139

Octagon House, 19, 31, 32, 183
"Ohio Gang," 99–100
O'Laughlin, Michael, 65
Old Stone House, 13

Palmer, A. Mitchell, 94
Pan American Union, 15, 82, 183
Panama Canal, 17, 87
Patent Office, U.S., 30
Patterson, Martha, 68
Patuxent River, 29
Payne, Lewis, 64, 65
Pearl Harbor, 127–28
Pennsylvania Avenue, 13, 19, 24, 39–41, 71, 97, 171, 174, 182
Pentagon, 130, 169, 183
Perkins, Frances, 121, 135
Philadelphia, 6, 15–16, 19, 31
Philippines, 132
Pittsburgh, 36–37
Point Four (foreign aid), 146–47
Pope (farmer), 12
Porter, David, 34
Potomac River, 3, 5–8, 12, 15, 22, 34, 52–53, 77, 112, 182
Drayton's ship becalmed in, 44
Maryland-Virginia conference on navigation of, 29

Memorial Bridge across, 97
northward crossing of, by Lee, 58
uselessness of, to ships of commerce, 36
Potsdam Conference, 139
President's House (White House), 9
President's Palace (White House), 13, 25
Profiles in Courage, 24
Progressive Party, 148
Prohibition Amendment, 94–95
Purple Heart, Order of, 9

Radical Republicans, 69–71
Randolph, A. Philip, 131
Randolph, John, 38
Rayburn, Sam, 126, 135
Rayburn Memorial, 112
Rayburn Office Building, 171
Reader's Digest, 131
Revolutionary War, 5, 7–8, 127
Reynolds v. Sims, 163
Richmond, Va., 55, 56, 60, 61
Rickover, Hyman, 159
Roberts, Owen, 119
Rock Creek Park, 43, 91
Rogers, Will, 91
Roosevelt, Eleanor, 108, 126, 127, 135–36
Roosevelt, Franklin D., 3, 20, 94, 108–09, 113–15, 121, 125–27, 135, 144
elected President, 109
"fireside chats" by, 113
second Inaugural Address by, 124
and Supreme Court, 115–19, 121
and World War II, 127–28, 130, 133–34, 138–39
See also New Deal
Roosevelt, Theodore, 17, 25, 77–78, 82–83, 108, 118
Root, Elihu, 18
Rosenthal, Joe, 137
"Rough Riders," 79
Royall, Anne, 34
Russia, 94, 142–43

Saarinen, Eero, 171
Sachs, Alexander, 138–39
St. John's Episcopal Church, 35
St. Matthew's Cathedral, 174

Salem Advocate, 47
Salinger, Pierre, 176
Sandburg, Carl, 67, 126
Scott, Winfield, 48, 50, 60
Securities Exchange Commission (SEC), 110
Senate, U.S., 20, 22, 26–27, 180
League of Nations rejected by, 91
trial in, of Andrew Johnson, 70–71
wealthy members of, 76
Senate Foreign Relations Committee, 90, 166
Senate Judiciary Committee, 117
Seward, William, 48–49, 64, 65
Shepherd, Alex, 73–76, 179
Sherman, William Tecumseh, 51, 61
Sherwood, Robert, 114
Sixteenth Amendment, 83
Slavery, Negro, 43–45, 61
Smith, Alfred E., 108
Smith, Margaret Bayard, 38
Smithson, James, 41–42
Smithsonian Institution, 20, 31, 41–43, 45, 73, 77, 96–97, 183
Snell, Bertrand, 110
Social Security, 110
Sorenson, Theodore, 169
Sousa, John Philip, 77
Southern Press, 44
Spangler, Edward, 65
Spanish-American War, 79
Spanish Civil War, 124
Spirit of St. Louis, 42, 97
Stalin, Josef, 134, 143, 157
"Star-Spangled Banner," 31
Stevens, Thaddeus, 69–71, 89–90
Stewart, J. George, 159
Stimson, Henry L., 135
Stowe, Harriet Beecher, 55
Sumners, Hatton, 117
Supreme Court, U.S., 22, 27, 98, 118, 160, 180
building of, 21, 115, 116, 183
dominated by Marshall, 27–28
"rights revolution" started by, 162 *ff.,* 178
and Roosevelt, Franklin D., 115–19, 121

Surratt, Mary, 65
Swope, Herbert Bayard, 143
Szilard, L., 138

Taft, William Howard, 73, 83
Taft Memorial, Robert A., 112
Taylor, Myron C., 119–20
Taylor, Zachary, 63
Teapot Dome scandal, 100
Teheran Conference, 134
Teller, Edward, 111, 138
Tennessee Valley Authority (TVA), 110
Thornton, William, 21–22, 30, 53
Three Sisters rocks, in Potomac, 22
Tiber Creek, 12, 19, 24, 52, 54, 62, 73–74
Tidal Basin, 182
Tippecanoe, Battle of, 63
Tocqueville, Alexis de, 141
Tomb of Unknown Soldier, 97, 98, 183
Treasury building, 40, 71, 171, 183
Truman, Harry S., 25–26, 134–36, 139, 141, 144–48, 151, 153–54, 156, 161, 167
  as landmark President, 152
Truman Doctrine, 145
Tydings, Millard, 151–52
Tyler, John, 45

Uncle Tom's Cabin, 55
Union Station, 81, 111, 154, 183
United Nations, 134, 142, 151, 166
United States Steel Corporation, 119–20
Unknown Soldier, 97, 98, 183
Urey, Harold, 151

Valley Forge, 8, 29
Van Buren, Martin, 33
Vandenburg, Arthur, 134, 145
V-E Day, 140
Versailles Treaty, 124
V-J Day, 140

Wall Street, power of, 68, 71
Wallace, Henry A., 126, 135
Wallach, Mayor, 74
War of 1812, 29–30, 32, 34
War on Poverty, 50, 159
War Production Board (World War II), 128

Warren, Earl, 118, 161–64, 178
Washburne, Elihu, 46
Washington, D.C.
  committee on beautification of (1902), 81
  description of (1800), 19–20
  in fear of Jackson (1829), 38–40
  George Washington University in, 111
  Howard University in, 72
  influenza epidemic in (1918), 87
  intolerance in (1920's), 98
  L'Enfant's plans for streets of, 12–13, 33
  Mrs. Lyndon B. Johnson's interest in, 178
  "March on" (1963), 162
  Negroes in, 43–45, 61–62, 72, 76, 82, 98, 111, 121–22, 131, 157–58, 171, 184–85
  Pentagon in, 130, 169
  population of, ebbs and flows, 33–34, 157
  rebuilding of, after War of 1812, 32
  self-rule absent in, 73, 75–76, 179–81, 184
  and Shepherd, 74, 179
  southwest quarter of, 171
  as theater of conflict during Civil War, 48, 51–55, 57–58
  veterans' march on (1932), 104–07
  visited by tourists, 186
  as world capital, 184–86
  and World War I, 86–87
  and World War II, 130–32, 134, 140
  Year 2000 Plan for, 170
  See also District of Columbia
Washington, George, 108
  as army officer, 5, 60
  bargain with Burnes, 14
  capital named for, 4
  and Capitol, 20
  commissioners appointed by, 15–16
  death of, 19
  greatness of, 108
  and L'Enfant, 5, 8–9, 13, 16–17

  opinion of capital, 5–6, 37, 78
  portrait of, in White House, 30
  statues of, 40–41
  as surveyor, 3–4, 5, 42
Washington, Lawrence, 3
Washington Circle, 41
Washington Evening Star, 74, 98
Washington Monument 9, 13, 41–42, 50, 52, 77, 183
Washington Post, 98, 148
Washington Post March, 77
Washington Senators (baseball team), 95
Watson, General, 139
Weaver, Robert C., 171, 185
Webster, Daniel, 38
Wedemeyer, General, 142
Westinghouse, George, 76
White City, Chicago's, 81
White House, 13–15, 19–20, 22, 24–25, 33–35
  Blue Room of, 59
  burned by British, 26, 30
  design of, 25–26
  East Room of, 40, 52, 173
  North Portico of, 26, 88
  restoration of, 26, 149
  South Portico of, 147
  See also Executive Mansion; President's House; President's Palace
Whitman, Walt, 56
Willard's Hotel, 45, 54, 73
Williams, Gluyas, 133
Wilson, Woodrow, 24, 91–93, 98, 102, 108, 118, 134–35, 144
  first wife of, 82, 84
  and First World War, 84–89
  Fourteen Points advocated by, 88–89
  and League of Nations, 90
  second wife of, 90
Winder Building, 50
Wolcott, Oliver, 20
World War I, 84–89
World War II, 126–33, 136–39, 153
Wright, Orville, 96–97
Wright, Wilbur, 96–97

Year 2000 Plan, 170

Zoo, Rock Creek Park, 43

ABOUT THE AUTHOR

Howard K. Smith, who appears regularly on ABC television, is one of America's foremost news commentators. Author of *Last Train From Berlin* (Knopf, 1942) and *The State of Europe* (Knopf, 1949), he writes a weekly column published in newspapers across the nation.

Mr. Smith, who studied at Oxford as a Rhodes Scholar, spent many years in Berlin, London, and other European cities as a foreign correspondent. With his wife and their two children, he settled in Washington in 1957. Enthusiastic about the city as a place to live, he considers himself one of Washington's permanent residents.

Howard K. Smith as moderator of a famous television debate between two Presidential candidates in 1960— John F. Kennedy (left) and Richard Nixon.